# POULTRY SHOWS
# &
# SHOWING

## JOSEPH BATTY

*Past President, Old English Game Club*
*Chairman, World Bantam & Poultry Society*

SPUR PUBLICATION BOOKS LTD
Beech Publishing House
7, Station Yard
Elsted Marsh
MIdhurst   GU29 0JT

*A Catalogue entry for this book is at the British Library*

Published in conjunction with the *World Bantam & Poultry Society*
(Registered Charity No. 1064283).
Re-introduction and development of the old breeds.

<u>In the International Poultry Library</u>

SPUR PUBLICATION BOOKS LTD
Beech Publishing House
7, Station Yard
Elsted Marsh
MIdhurst   GU29 0JT

# CONTENTS

## PREFACE

I have felt the need of a book on exhibiting poultry for many years. Moreover, many young fanciers have enquired for an introductory work which explained the procedures and helped them to understand the official Standards, which are excellent, but rather daunting to the newcomer.

Once started the area expanded until the all the main requirements are touched upon. Accordingly, I believe that the would-be poultry judge may find the detailed analysis and faults, with many examples from winners at shows, of great value.

My thanks are offered to many fanciers who assisted in providing information. Without the body of wisdom available it would be impossible for anyone to outline the history of this great hobby and then go on to describe present day procedures.

I still remember the days when, as a boy, my father took me to shows held in Barnsley and Penistone. What an interesting, fascinating place for any young person interested in livestock. Keeping bantams can provide hours of enjoyment as well as being profitable.

*With Best Wishes for Success!*

Joseph Batty

**January, 1999**

**The Author Judging at a Poultry Show**

# 1

# HISTORY
# OF
# THE SHOWS

**Harvey Brown a Young Fancier in 1914**
With his winning Wyandotte Bantams

# HISTORY OF THE SHOWS

## The Scene

Although formal displays have been known for generations, it appears to have been the Victorians (1837-1901) and their counterparts in the USA and other countries, which started the shows we know today.

Many personalities were involved in breeding birds and animals to show standard. For poultry showing, there were the people who were to go down in history as famous breeders or writers. In Britain these included:

Charles Darwin, Sir Walter Gilbey, *Bart,* W Wingfield, G W Johnson, T B Tegetmeier, Harrison Weir, Lewis Wright, J W Ludlow, Ernest Wippell, W F Entwisle and then J F Entwisle, William Cook, Sir Edward Brown, Rev. T W Sturges, and others. More recently there are personalities such as W Powell-Owen, Rex Woods and Sam Lean.

When poultry keeping and showing became popular it was fashionable to be in the *Fancy*; Queen Victoria and the peers of the realm gave the movement respectability and backing.

Before that time the early shows had been rather informal events, usually held in the Northern English counties, especially Lancashire and Yorkshire, where the qualities of *sound plumage and the correct type* were the basis of the judging. In the South the main interest was in the table qualities –white skin and plump flesh with an acceptable flavour. This concentration on utility was quite correct in many ways, because once exhibition qualities *only* were looked for the egg laying properties went in decline.

Eventually the two sides came together and by that time the heyday of exhibiting had arrived. Often, also, the prices of prize birds was beyond those who took an interest in a few head of poultry— the working man to whom the birds were an interesting hobby.

### Early Minor Shows

The early local shows created interest in particular breeds which then became national breeds when transportation was improved. In the very early days, before trains were developed, along with the national rail track, the exhibitions had to be restricted to local farms and public houses.*

Breeds which became known, for example, as Hamburghs, were known locally as "Pheasants" or "Mooneys" and had been established for more than three centuries.

Judging was on specific features relating to comb, colour, legs and feathering. This was the foundation of the judging by standards and was in the North of England, mainly in Lancashire and Yorkshire, whereas in Cumbria there was the interest, which still exists, in Game Fowl. It was on Cleator Moor in Cumbria that Old English Game bantams were reinstated as show birds, having being pushed out by the newer creation of 'Modern Game'.

---

**THE CRYSTAL PALACE (Opposite)**
*This famous building was erected by Sir J Paxton in 1853/54 at the enormous cost of £1.5m. It was an exotic surrounding for all kinds of pastimes and amusements, including poultry shows.*

---

* The first primitive trains were around in 1830 and reached their heyday with the Flying Scotsman in 1895. Today motor vehicles (mainly cars) take birds to shows with the owners.

Further South in Northamptonshire, under the sponsorship of Earl Spencer, shows were being arranged for Table Poultry, fowls which had to be "plump, deep, long and capacious in body, with almost white legs", a type which reflected the Dorking and Surrey fowls.

### The First Official Shows

The first show in 1845 was attended by fanciers who were keeping the *Old English Game types* of fowl, albeit some of them had been imported!

**Dorkings**
**Hamburghs**
**Sussex or Kent**
**Malays**
**Polands**
**Spanish**
**Surrey**
**AOV**
**Bantams - Gold or Silver Spangled (probably Sebrights)**
**Bantams - Black or White (probably Rosecombs)**

The judges were John Baily ( who later became an acknowledged authority and wrote books) , with Yarrell, the ornithologist, and George Fisher an expert on pigs.

Hanson Weir* who was to become famous as an artist and author on poultry was present and at that time he would be in his twenty-first year, having been an animal and bird painter from around 18 years of age, but actually starting at the early age of 5 years. In *Our Animal Brothers,* edited by Edith Carrington in 1906, it was noted that on his fifth birthday, on a farm in Pembury, Kent, he was found drawing poultry. In fact, he was later to become a poultry judge and was to witness the great development of the shows until his death 60 years later.

*A Biography on this famous artist and poultry fancier (1824 - 1906) is in the course of preparation by the author of this book.

R.W. THRUPP, PHOTO.    BIRMINGHAM

**Harrison Weir in 1872**
**A Victorian Artist in his Prime**

**He recorded what he saw so that we**
**have a record of how the birds looked.**

• • • • • • • • • • • • • • • • • • • • • • • • • • • • • • • • • • • •

As will be seen from the text, Harrison Weir was at the first major poultry show and, as a result, he met others, such as W B Tegetmeier, who also played a major part in developing the shows. The two became well known to each other and were fellow members of the **Savage Club,** and Harrison Weir illustrated *The Poultry Book* (Tegetmeier) a major work on poultry keeping, as well as his own mammoth work *Our Poultry.*

The next show was at the Zoological Gardens, two years later and, again, was very successful. The theme was the *development of utility poultry* so Dorkings, Sussex and Surrey fowl were to the front of the entries. In passing, it is interesting to note that the Sussex breed did not become a standardised breed until 1903 and the related Old Kent Fowl was never given this recognition. Yet this was a long established breed similar to the Dorking type. In fact, it was only the prompting by Sir Edward Brown at a meeting held in Lewes in 1903 that the fanciers of Sussex decided to form the Sussex Poultry Club.*

### Early Major Poultry Shows

The first show proper appears to have taken place in 1845 at the London Zoological Gardens and from this point there was great activity developing the many breeds and the relative standards.

Eastern counties became known for their ability to organise shows which handled, arranged judging, awarded prizes and then returned the birds safely to their owners. These were:

*1. Birmingham (from 1848).*
In normal years this show handled over 2000 entries.

*2. In London.*
The first major show was held at Crystal Palace (burnt down in 1936) and then various other venues and currently at the Agricultural Centre at Stoneleigh in Warwickshire, and Stafford, organized by the Poultry Club and the Federation of Breed Clubs respectively.

---

* See *Sussex & Dorking Fowls*, J Batty, which covers the history of these breeds and modern management, with colour plates  of a number, including the Old Kent Fowl.

**A Drawing of a Black Red Cock completed in 1853 by Harrison Weir drawn for one of Tegetmeier's books.**

Note the style of the bird, which we can be sure was the original type as depicted by the Game fanciers when they started the Oxford Old English Fowl Club. Sadly many of the so-called *Oxford Game* lack elegance, are short in limb, narrow and long in body and have weak tails. Judges should weed out the non-standard types by refusing to give prizes to them..

# Birmingham Show

The show developed very rapidly, adding classes and subdividing them, until there were around 100 in existence, with more than 2000 entries. All this occurred within a period of about 20 years.

At this time (1868) the Asian breeds such as Cochins and Brahmas had been assimilated into the poultry world with enthusiasm and excitement. However, the Dorkings with 8 classes were still very important. The Cochins had 12 classes and Brahmas had 8. Hamburghs were also well in evidence with 10 classes. Game Fowl had 16 classes.

Bantams included Gold and Silver laced (Sebrights), White clean legged, Black clean legged (Rosecombs) and any other variety which included Frizzled, Japanese, Booted, and Rumpless. However, in all there were only 5 classes for bantams.

W B Tegetmeier, naturalist and poultry breeder, a friend of Charles Darwin, won first prize with a Rumpless. He was to make a valuable contribution to the furtherance of exhibition poultry breeding.

The Birmingham Show went on for many years until, eventually, only one major Show could be sustained and this fell to venues in London, starting at the Crystal Palace. This incredible building was completed for the Great Exhibition of 1851and continued to house the poultry shows until it was burnt down in 1936. In 1899 there had been 21 shows.

## The Crystal Palace Show

The race for supremacy in the show world was now on and the Crystal Palace authorities took various steps to improve standards and interest. In 1870 the rules were modified to instruct judges to consider: *"condition, quality, beauty of plumage, purity of lace and uniformity of markings and comb and other characteristics"*.

In 1899 there were 3,487 entries and only 13 judges to

**An Early Drawing by Harrison Weir at a Major Show.**
Note the difference in plumage in the breeds from those shown in modern times.

compare them and award prizes.  In short, the response was overwhelming, no doubt encouraged by the impact of the new fowls from the USA as well as breeds which had been newly introduced by crossing the new breeds.

The Mediterranean breeds, as well as  Indian Game, Plymouth Rocks, Orpingtons and Wyandottes were *not* included, but were to come shortly after.  This is quite surprising for breeds like Minorcas because they had been kept in England from quite early on. Their bantams also came on the scene.

## British Dairy Farmers Association
This body started organising shows in 1876 and included poultry.  This grew rapidly and in 1878 there were some 60 classes.  There were 450 exhibitors and they made entries for 984 birds, a tremendous turnout.  The schedule was along lines similar to the Birmingham and Crystal Palace shows.

---

### *OPPOSITE*
**Table Showing Number of Classes for each Breed.
Shows held at Crystal Palace 1870 - 1889.**

**NOTES:   (a) Four classes, Black Cochin or Langshan.**

**(b) Additional class for Dark, Mottled Breasted cockerel.**

**(c) Six entries were La Fleche.**

**(d) Andalusian and Minorca.**

**(e) Competed against Black Cochins, see (a).**

**(f) and  (g), Now named Rosecombs.**

### TABLE SHOWS NUMBER OF CLASSES ALLOCATED TO EACH BREED AT THE CRYSTAL PALACE SHOW, 1870–1889

It emphasises that, with the exception of the Rhode Island Red and Sussex fowls, all the popular breeds were imported or created within the first 45 years of active poultry interest.

| Breed. | 1870 | 1871 | 1872 | 1874 | 1875 | 1876 | 1877 | 1878 | 1879 | 1889 |
|---|---|---|---|---|---|---|---|---|---|---|
| **LARGE** | | | | | | | | | | |
| Dorking | 7 | 8 | 10 | 10 | 12 | 12 | 11 | 11 | 11 | 12 |
| Cochin | 7 | 10 | 12 | 15 | 15 | 15 | 15 | 17 | 17(a) | 12 |
| Brahma | 6 | 8 | 8 | 8 | 9(b) | 9 | 9 | 9 | 9 | 8 |
| Spanish | 3 | 4 | 4 | 4 | 4 | 4 | 4 | 4 | 4 | 4 |
| Houdan | 2 | 2 | 4 | 4 | 4 | 4 | 4 | 4 | 4 | 4 |
| French AOV. | 2(c) | 2 | — | — | — | — | — | — | — | 2 |
| Hamburgh | 5 | 5 | 9 | 10 | 10 | 10 | 10 | 10 | 10 | 10 |
| Game | 6 | 8 | 12 | 12 | 12 | 11 | 11 | 16 | 16 | 20 |
| Polish | 3 | 3 | 6 | 6 | 6 | 6 | 6 | 6 | 8 | 6 |
| Malay | 1 | 1 | 1 | 1 | 1 | 1 | 2 | 2 | 2 | 4 |
| A.O. Variety | 1 | 1 | 1 | 1 | 1 | 1 | 1 | 1 | 1 | 1 |
| Creve Coeur | – | — | 4 | 4 | 4 | 4 | 4 | 4 | 4 | — |
| Silkie | – | — | 1 | 1 | 1 | 1 | — | — | — | — |
| Leghorn | – | — | — | — | 2 | 4 | 4 | 4 | 4 | 6 |
| Andalusian | – | — | — | — | 1 | 2 | 2 | 2 | 2(d) | 4 |
| Langshan | – | — | — | — | — | 2 | 1 | 3 | (e) | 4 |
| Sultan | – | — | — | — | — | — | — | 1 | 2 | 4 |
| Indian Game | – | — | — | — | — | — | — | — | — | 4 |
| Minorca | – | — | — | — | — | — | — | — | — | 6 |
| Plymouth Rock | – | — | — | — | — | — | — | — | — | 4 |
| Orpington | – | — | — | — | — | — | — | — | — | 2 |
| Scotch Grey | – | — | — | — | — | — | — | — | —. | 2 |
| Wyandotte | – | — | — | — | — | — | — | — | — | 3 |
| **BANTAMS.** | | | | | | | | | | |
| Game | 6 | 8 | 9 | 9 | 9 | 8 | 8 | 8 | 8 | 17 |
| Black | 1 | 1 | 1 | 1 | 1 | 1 | 1 | 1 | 1 | 4(f) |
| A.O. Variety | 1 | 1 | 1 | 1 | 1 | 1 | 1 | 1 | 1 | 2 |
| Sebright | – | 1 | 1 | 1 | 1 | 1 | 1 | 1 | 1 | 4 |
| White | – | — | 1 | — | — | — | — | — | — | 4(g) |
| White Booted | – | — | — | 1 | 1 | 1 | 1 | — | — | — |
| Nankin | – | — | — | 1 | — | — | — | — | — | — |
| Booted, A.C. | – | — | — | — | — | — | — | 1 | — | 2 |
| Japanese | – | — | — | — | — | — | — | — | 1 | 2 |
| Cuckoo | – | — | — | — | — | — | — | — | — | 2 |
| Pekin | – | — | — | — | — | — | — | — | — | 6 |
| Malay | – | — | — | — | — | — | — | — | — | 2 |

# LORDS, LADIES AND GENTLEMEN

The upsurge in interest was very much aided and abetted by royal patronage from Queen Victoria downwards to the Lords and Ladies of the realm. Her Majesty had received seven Cochins as early as 1843 and she was involved in the show scene. These birds were given the Gold Medal at the Royal Dublin Show. Her support gave the lead required for the great poultry show boom which followed.

The patronage of the shows by distinguished persons presented the correct image and encouraged all people of importance to be seen at these great exhibitions. Very high prices were asked and obtained for prize exhibits. Those birds winning cups were sold for as much as £165. Such prices were astronomical and could only be afforded by the wealthy.

Birds were even sent from the USA to Queen Victoria, amidst great publicity and controversy. George P Burnham, a dealer in poultry presented "Brahmas" to her Majesty in 1853 and these were called *Grey Shanghae Fowl*. Others followed at substantial prices.

**Light Bramas sent by George P Burnham to Queen Victoria**
**The publicity in *The Illustrated London News*, drawn by Harrison Weir ,**
**caused great excitement in the Poultry Fancy.**

## DOMESTIC POULTRY: PATRONS

HER GRACE THE DUCHESS OF BEAUFORT
HER GRACE THE DUCHESS OF MARLBOROUGH
HER GRACE THE DUCHESS OF SUTHERLAND
THE MOST HON. THE MARCHIONESS OF HERTFORD
THE RIGHT HON. THE COUNTESS OF CHESTERFIELD
THE RIGHT HON. THE COUNTESS OF COVENTRY
THE RIGHT HON. THE COUNTESS OF DARTMOUTH
THE RIGHT HON. THE DOWAGER COUNTESS OF AYLESFORD
THE RIGHT HON. THE COUNTESS OF CRAVEN
THE RIGHT HON. THE COUNTESS OF BRADFORD
THE RIGHT HON. THE COUNTESS HOWE
THE RIGHT HON. THE COUNTESS SOMERS
THE RIGHT HON. THE COUNTESS OF LICHFIELD
THE RIGHT HON. THE COUNTESS OF YARMOUTH
THE RIGHT HON. THE VISCOUNTESS COMBERMERE
THE RIGHT HON. THE VISCOUNTESS HILL
THE RIGHT HON. THE LADY SHERBORNE
THE RIGHT HON. LADY BAGOT
THE RIGHT HON. LADY HATHERTON
THE RIGHT HON. LADY LEIGH
THE RIGHT HON. LADY WENLOCK
THE RIGHT HON. LADY GWYDYR
THE LADY EMILY FOLEY
THE LADY LOUISA COTES
THE LADY EMILY KINGSCOTE
THE LADY CHARLOTTE EGERTON
THE LADY GEORGINA VERNON
THE HON. MRS. AUGUSTUS CALTHORPE
THE HON. MRS. A. BAILLIE HAMILTON
THE HON. MRS. COLVILE
THE HON. MRS. SUGDEN
THE HON. MISS DOUGLAS PENNANT
THE HON. MRS. ARBUTHNOTT
THE HON. MRS. HOWARD
THE HON. MRS. OAKLEY
DOWAGER LADY MORDAUNT
LADY ISHAM
LADY LAWLEY

**A Page from the Birmingham Show official catalogue, 1878**
The patronage was an indication of the social status of the early exhibitors.

## Speckled Sussex
**Even Speckling; mahogany/burgundy colour, with black tail.**

From the start, try to analyse the essentials and make sure the stock comply. They will not win unless they fit into the standard requirements. Many breeders spend years 'perfecting' a breed only to find that they cannot achieve the winning shape.

For full details see *Sussex & Dorking Fowls,* J Batty, available from the publishers.

# 2

# DEVELOPMENT
# OF THE
# BREEDS

**Early Dorkings    (Harrison Weir)**
These were profitable fowl, but with crosses to improve size lost their
activeness and became purely show birds.

### The Famous MacNab

This famous cock who was painted and feted because of his winning at shows.

He was owned by Lord Dewar and won the championship at the Crystal Palace Show in 1924 with a total entry of 6,530 birds.

*The breeder and exhibitor is trying to achieve as near perfection as possible.*

# DEVELOPMENT OF STANDARD BREEDS

## First Standards

For shows to be contemplated there had to be the development of standard or "pure" breeds. This was not an overnight achievement because starting from scratch, there were the following:

1. Barn-yard poultry.

2. Table poultry bred for fattening for London markets, Sussex and Surrey Fowl.
3. Recognised breeds which were to become the foundation stone of many new breeds.

*These included Old English Game, Dorkings, Scots Greys, and Scots Dumpies. Some French breeds such as the Houdan were also in existence from an early date. Bantams were also in existence and may have been there from very early times; Rosecombs, Sebrights and OEG bantams\*.*

4. Imports which came as distinct type; most were often modified as a result of the desire to improve for showing. The Mediterranean breeds, Silkies, Malays and Aseel were brought in. These were followed by the soft feathered Asian breeds such as Brahmas, Cochins and Langshans which would have a considerable impact on the development of new breeds and shows. Frizzles were also in at the start.

---

*\* Titles exist on all these breeds tracing the history—available from the publisher.*

## Personalities Involved

There were many personalities involved in establishing the first *standards*. Some were judges, others fanciers, a few were authors, and the balance were artists. Slowly but surely the evolution of the standards took place; instead of the personal opinions of the judges there had to be written descriptions and pictorial representations (drawings and photographs).

Terms used had to be described; shapes, colours and other characteristics had to be listed and detailed. Only in this way would it be possible to show the main characteristics for each breed which, in turn, would allow comparisons to be made.

Judging is very much the process of deciding to which degree the required features are present, thus enabling points to be awarded so that those with the most points can be adjudged the winners.

The persons involved in establishing the early standards including the following, were:

1. **J Dixon.** He judged from 1856.

2. **E Hewitt.** He judged from 1854 and went on for 30 years.

3. **R Tebay.** He judged from 1858.

4. **W B Tegetmeier**. A naturalist, journalist and author. Judged from the early days and cut out many malpractices. His Standards gave 15 points, which were too inflexible.

5. **W F Entwisle.** Breeder extraordinary who also drew up standards which formed the basis for later standards modified by Lewis Wright.

6. **Harrison Weir.** Kept birds and went to shows, but judging commitments were limited.

7. **J W Ludlow.** Judge, fancier and leading artist.

**W W Broomhead judging at the Crystal Palace Show.**
He was a judge and major author as well as editing the standards (see text)

**8. Lewis Wright.** Limited judging, but committed as Editor, writer and author on poultry matters. Collected the details for the foundation of the standards.

**9. Wm W Broomhead** who remodelled the standards and judged at shows.

*Cont.*

**10. The Modern standards then came.  C G May,** edited a new version,  published by a commercial publisher. **David Hawksworth** also was involved in this version, taking over from May.   The latest editor is **Victoria Roberts  (1997)** ; she has included many foreign breeds in fowl and domesticated ducks and geese— for the first time it also has many coloured photographs in the book proper, instead of a few coloured paintings which were out of date. These photographs have to be used with great care for many do not comply with the written standards! They can thus be quite misleading. This is the fifth edition of the new issue.

The first *standards* were published in 1864 for the first British Poultry Club which foundered amidst much acrimony. A new club was founded in 1877, being suggested by Sir Edward Brown. From this date new standards were brought into use.

In recent times,  innovators like Rex Woods and Will Burdett, both past Presidents,  have carried out improvements in the organization of shows and breeds.Malcolm Thompson has improved the image of the Fancy by his skilful development of the *Poultry Club Year Book*. In addition, some breeders have been outstanding in raising the image of their own breeds and, whilst these are too numerous to list, special mention should be made of Sam Lean who has bred OEG bantams to an extremely high standard.

All this has helped to raise the standard expected of show winners and has led to admiration which is world wide. Many clubs in Australia, New Zealand and other countries have also helped to improve the breeds and much information and photographs of winning birds have been sent to be included in books. They have now published their own standards as well.

Unfortunately, and inevitably, there are individuals who do not serve the common good by refusing to answer letters or failing to co-operate in ventures which appear to interfere with their own ego-building so the Fancy suffers. Such individuals should not be tolerated in any capacity, but especially so when they hold positions of Secretary of clubs or other high office.

Newcomers coming into the Fancy cannot understand when he or she cannot get a reply or acknowledgement to an enquiry and a possible recruit to the hobby is lost for ever. Fortunately, the great majority of local poultry societies and breed clubs, do all they can to encourage poultry fanciers.

**W B Tegetmeier (1816-1912)**
He lived to a great age and did much for the Poultry Fancy.
Charles Darwin was one of his colleagues as was Harrison Weir.

The task of developing the standards was left to those above 1, 3 and 4. The latter (Tegetmeier) edited the first *Standards* and also wrote a large comprehensive book bringing together the details provided by breed clubs and others, in which these standards were included, and the illustrations came from the hand of Harrison Weir.

A major difficulty with the very early standards was the total of 15 points for each standard which proved to be inflexible. Therefore, although these were not adopted they provided the foundation stone for the future standards. These came about at the Poultry Convention in New York held in 1872, but instead of the 15 points in total, this became 100.

In 1886 the new (partial) British standards became available under the auspices of the Poultry Club. These were the originals modified by Lewis Wright who had made a special study of the birds over many years (*Journal of Horticulture).*

Undoubtedly the artists of the day also played a part in showing judges and the public the different breeds and their features. J W Ludlow an idealist, provided his version of the "ideal" birds. They appeared in *Bantams* (Entwisle) and *The Illustrated Book of Poultry* (Lewis Wright).

Harrison Weir was most critical of some of the developments and what he termed the "mongrelising" of the breeds.and was not afraid to pronounce his views. His birds were drawn as he saw them, true to life.

Later Ernest Wippell drew some excellent "models" and on the photographic side, which developed quite fast in the 20th century, A Rice took more photographs of prize winning birds than anyone else; in fact, *The Feathered World Year Book,* in the 1920s and '30s were packed with his portraits.

---

**OPPOSITE: The title page from *The British Poultry Standards.* This book first came out in 1901**

# THE
# POULTRY CLUB
# STANDARDS

CONTAINING A COMPLETE DESCRIPTION OF ALL
THE RECOGNIZED BREEDS AND VARIETIES OF
FOWLS, BANTAMS, DUCKS, GEESE, AND TURKEYS

Edited by
## WILLIAM W. BROOMHEAD

*SEVENTH EDITION.*

**LONDON:**
William Rice, Hon. Secretary and Treasurer,
The Poultry Club, 3 Ludgate Broadway, E.C.4
1926.

## OFFICIAL STANDARDS DEVELOPMENT
As indicated, the development of official standards was a slow tortuous business and came as result of co-ordination by the British Poultry Club and, abroad, the American Poultry Association.

At first the main judges exerted considerable influence on the type of birds winning prizes and, even with the early standards available, there was lack of accord in the judging. The leaders J Dixon, E Hewitt, R Teebay and W B Tegetmeier appear to have had the main responsibilities, with the latter doing all he could to ensure that mal-practices were stamped out, raised the fairness at shows so that the best exhibits won.

The individual breed clubs, some of which existed from quite early times, began to exercise more control over what should be included in the breed standard for its own breed, with the Poultry Club co-ordinating the efforts. The Sebright Club under Sir John Sebright, Bart*, was formed some 200 years ago and was a forerunner of the later clubs which followed. Others were formed until all the major breeds were covered. Today, those without a club come under the Rare Breeds Poultry Society.

### The Poultry Club Standards
The Standards were issued under the editorship of W B Tegetmeier in 1864 *with 15 points as the basis for judging*. (see earlier in this chapter). Their importance is considerable because the main format is still used today.

An abortive standard (*The Lewis Wright Standard*) was prepared in 1886, but, according to H Easom Smith** was not issued, but was made available in 1901. However, the *verso* (copyright) page of the title states that the standards were issued from 1886,

---

* For a detailed account on how the Sebright bantam was developed see *The Sebright Bantam*, Joseph Batty.
** *Modern Poultry Development*, Spur Publications, Liss, 1976. H Easom Smith, a Past President of the Poultry Club, was an influential poultry journalist and author of *Bantams for Everone*, which went into a number of editions.

but the variation is explained by William W Broomhead in the seventh edition issued in 1927. This small pocket book went on being published until 1954 when an entirely new edition was prepared by C G May and was reissued a number of times.

The latest version (new 5th edition), edited by Victoria Roberts, is larger than any previous British Standard. Despite its faults—some serious omissions in colour photographs, and the anomalies that still exist in the use of *TYPE* to mean different things, the book is a considerable improvement on previous editions.

A summary of the need and purpose of standards has been summed up by William Broomhead, in *The Poultry Club Standards,* as follows:

PROBABLY the first attempt in this country to form Standards for exhibition poultry in anything approaching a uniform style was undertaken by the late Lewis Wright. In 1871 or thereabouts he wrote his great work *The Ilustrated Book of Poultry.* The plan selected was not adopted by Mr. Wright, however, until he had carefully studied the awards of those recognized authorities of his day who acted as judges at the bulk of the shows. And even then, to quote his own words, " It was only by slow degrees and by laborious analysis, which, throughout, demanded a tedious mathematical investigation," that he was enabled to reduce them to figures, to schedule the points for judging certain breeds of poultry. One has merely to glance at some of the original standards to imagine what such a task meant; and perhaps the finest example is seen in the " Value of Points in Light Brahmas: The Cock." Here were shown what may well be termed " distinct defects " to the total of twenty-two, some of them, such as " stain of white in deaf ear," " striping in saddle," etc., being pointed as low as 2, while the highest, " impure colour of white," was only 10, albeit the " perfect bird " scored 100 points, as now. Even those earliest Standards, nevertheless, crude, as they were afterwards, acknowledged to be, were useful in fixing and crystallizing ideas that formerly were very vague.

The idea of those " Schedules for Judging," as they were termed, was to act as Standards for others; and they were set up, as was patent, by the judges, and not, as some suppose, by Specialist Clubs. These scales, as far as anv scales could do so, represented modern judging; hence they offered sound and accurate guide for private study. It was in this way, therefore, by demonstrating the most important points for which poultry were being awarded prizes at the exhibitions, that the amateur could hope to breed birds to the ideal set up.

## CHARACTERS OF DORKINGS,

*As given in the English and American Standards of Excellence.*

### GENERAL SHAPE.

#### THE COCK.

*Beak*—Rather short and stout.

*Comb*—Either single or rose; if single, erect, straight, serrated, free from side sprigs ; if rose-combed, square in front, straight on the head, without hollow in the middle, large peak behind, inclining very slightly upwards.

*Head*—Neat.

*Wattles*—Broad, stout, rounded on the lower edge.

*Neck*—Very taper and well hackled.

*Breast*—Very deep, broad, and full. Breast-bone long.

*Body*—Large, deep, compact, and plump, the back, belly, breast, and behind almost forming a square.

*Back*—Very broad.

*Wings*—Large.

*Tail*—Very large, expanded, feathers broad and carried well up.

*Sickle Feathers and Tail Coverts*—Long, broad, sound, and well arched.

*Thighs*—Short, stout, and straight.

*Legs*—Straight, short, stout, clean, and perfectly free from feathers, spurred on the inside.

*Feet*—Five-toed, the extra or supernumerary toe well developed, distinctly separated from the others, and pointing upwards.

*Carriage and Appearance*—Noble, bulky, and grand.

#### THE HEN.

*Beak*—Rather short.

*Comb*—If single, to be well developed, and falling over one side of the face ; if rose, square in front, straight on the head, peak behind inclining slightly upwards.

*Wattles*—Broad, rounded on the lower edge.

*Head*—Neat.

*Neck*—Short and taper.

*Breast*—Very deep, broad, and full.

*Body*—Large, compact, plump, and deep.

*Back*—Broad.

*Wings*—Large.

*Tail*—Large, expanded, the feathers broad.

*Thighs*—Short and stout.

*Legs*—Short, straight, thick, and strong.

*Feet*—Five-toed, the extra toe well developed, distinctly separated from the others, and inclining upwards.

*Carriage and Appearance*—Bulky.

### COLOURED DORKINGS.

The colour in these not material, provided the birds match in the pen.

#### Points in Coloured Dorkings.

|  | English Standard. | American Standard. |
|---|---|---|
| Size | 5 | 35 |
| Head | } 2 | 5 |
| Comb | | 5 |
| Legs, Feet, and Toes | 2 | 15 |
| Symmetry | 4 | 25 |
| Condition | 2 | 15 |
|  | 15 | 100 |

#### Disqualifications.

Birds without the fifth toe, or with crooked backs, wry tails, combs not matching in the pen, legs of any other colour except white.

## Extract from the Standard for Dorkings (Tegetmeier)

Note the 15 points which proved too restricting  for judges; later amended to  100  like the American.

In my opinion, however, they were much too complicated to be of real service to the beginner. The points were altogether too numerous, too split up, if I may use such a term. For instance, harking back to the Light Brahma cock, there were eight distinct " cuts" for colour, viz., tail, legs, deaf ears (now known as lobes, or ear lobes), breast, hock, fluff, white, and " Other defects of colour," making a grand total of 34 points to be deducted out of a possible 100 for the perfect bird.

In those days, admittedly, there were nothing like the number of poultry fanciers that one meets now. Nearly all of them were " big guns." The rank and file formed a small percentage of exhibitors, which, after all, was not very surprising, since the " Schedules for Judging" were most formidable objects, and likely to discourage rather than encourage the beginner !

The first break away from the old order of things was in 1901 when the late Tom Threlford edited the second edition of the " Poultry Club Standards." That issue included the Standards adopted by seven Specialist Clubs, while the Editor had the assistance of many well-known fanciers, most of whom, alas ! are no longer with us. Mr. Threlford also edited the third edition — printed as the second, by the way, presumably because the existence of the first (1886) issue was forgotten—which was published in 1905. It was practically a reprint of the second, with the addition of Standards for four new varieties of Wyandottes, and others of breeds which had come into prominence.

My first editing of the Standards was in 1910—the fourth edition. I undertook the work because the publication did not satisfy me as being thoroughly representative of the great central Club. My endeavour was to preserve throughout all the Standards, a uniformity of pattern and order, and, as far as possible, of phrasings to use the simplest terms available so that those who can read may follow. To avoid the stereo-typed phrasing and often useless repetitions of the ordinary Specialist Clubs' Standards, therefore, I rewrote the vast majority of them. But everything necessary to that end was done in most cordial co-operation and consultation with those clubs; and the minimum amount of verbal alteration or transposition was made which would secure uniformity of system throughout, and thus assist the novice the better to understand the terms used, since, be it remembered, it was for him that the Standards were originally compiled.

The first aim of any Standard must be to describe correctly the varieties treated of, and to present them in language as simple and comprehensive as possible. One innovation I made was to omit the word " size." For instance, to describe size as " about 6 lb." is obviously absurd. Weights are given, but even that is a doubtful goal. The fancier should not breed for mere weight, and the tendency to do so has spoilt more than one breed. Fancy fowls are not judged by weight, except in special classes for Old English Game; and " the larger the better, provided always type is fully maintained," is, in my opinion, desirable in most breeds except Bantams* . I also divided the breeds into sitters and non-sitters, since it is hardly practicable to define a standard size. This feature, I have reason to know, has been of service to the novice, since there must be few, if any, who enter the Poultry Fancy, who are unable to distinguish between the one and the other. In fowls of the non-sitting class there should be a greater development at the posterior than at the breast; in sitting breeds, the breast is deep and full, the development being as prominent there as at the stern. In the 1910 edition, too, instead of following the usual style of describing the head as distinct from the parts necessary to form it, I introduced the word " skull," classing skull, beak;, eyes, comb, face, earlobes, and wattles—and crest and muffling, too, where such were necessary—under the section devoted to " Head."

Then, again, the word " disqualifications" has rightly been omitted from the Poultry Club Standards; and points that would necessitate a bird being excluded from competition, and which do not imply any fraud or fraudulent practices, have been tabulated as " serious defects." It may be as well to mention that fraudulent practices, as defined in the Poultry Club Show Rules, include, among others, the following:—*Trimming, the removal of foul or superfluous feathers, or the insertion of supplementary ones; the cutting in any way of the comb, the lobes, or the wattles (Game breeds excepted); the staining or otherwise colouring, of the legs, the lobes, or the plumage or the trimming thereof.*

In short, any artificial alteration is a disqualification in all varieties.

In the Standards included in this volume the ' Scale of Points' shows the fair proportionate value which general opinion considers should be given to any defects in the various points, and that being so, it is hoped that qualified judges will recognize and respect them and not violently upset them by notions of their own. It is not likely, nor perhaps desirable, that birds should be systematically " scored " by them, and prizes awarded accordingly. " The proper use of a Standard, " once wrote the late Lewis Wright, " is not to give birds a score, but to place them in correct order of merit. It must never be forgotten that small deductions or cuts for conspicuous defects cannot do this. The figures in the ' points ' following are meant to express what ought

---

* The question of weight is controversial because there is a general size for a breed and a marked shortfall or over weight cannot be ignored. So, although accepting the principle proposed, the weight must be considered. In the USA it is regarded as a 'breed characteristic' and included in a penalty for any shortcoming on this factor. (Author)

to be deducted from the Standard 100 points for as much fault in the points named as can exist, and still leave a bird in competition. Not as much as possible, by any means; for instance, if the point be comb, and 10 are allowed, a comb bad beyond a certain degree would throw a bird entirely out, and not be deducted at all. It is meant that if the comb is really about as bad as still leaves the bird any chance at all, the I0 should be deducted; and less for slighter defects—perhaps even only one or half a point for very slight defect. But for serious and evident faults serious cuts must be made if the Standard is to perform its function."

There is little to add to the foregoing quotation. At poultry exhibitions throughout the British Isles birds are judged by comparison with each other; and, although mentally scored by the judge, the score-card system for Fancy stock has not been adopted in this country. A proportionate number of points is allotted to certain characteristics, but it must be left to the judge's discretion as to how many of them he shall deduct for faults in varying degrees. There is no greater advocate of the use of the Standards than I, and in my opinion a thorough knowledge of them is highly desirable by all who undertake the exhibitng and judging of poultry. Nevertheless, all of us cannot think alike; hence it is that the scores under different judges must vary to some slight degree. Then, again, it should be clearly understood that there are no specimens in existence which conform in every respect with the Standards set forth in these pages. The particulars given  in each case represent the ideal bird which breeders should strive to reproduce in as high a degree as possible; but in doing so to keep within reason and not breed any point to excess.

*This summary is a shortened version of the Introduction to the Standards (see page 25) and lays down some very important principles of judging which are still applicable today. Reference will be made to these later when the actual judging process is explained. However, it will be noted that there is little chance of breeding the absolutely perfect bird, but judges should not take advantage of the important task they are given to award  points for exaggerated features and, at the same time,  ignore much more balanced birds which do not have the <u>key  factors </u>to a high degree as described on page 40.*

## STANDARDS FOR BANTAMS

Generally the standards for bantams which have the equivalent in large fowl are laid down along identical or very similar lines. The work of W F Entwisle laid a foundation for bantams bred down from large and for true bantams and these were used to provide a supplement to the normal poultry standards book. There was at one time The British Bantam Association headed by  W H Silk who did much to further the Fancy.

In the 1930s onwards there was Major G T Williams who kept and showed a great variety of bantams from his location in Cornwall.

## AMERICAN STANDARDS

In the USA there is an American Bantam Association which represents the bantam fancy. Fred P Jeffrey, author of ***Bantam Breeding & Genetics,*** was a leading figure up to quite recently. Although the American Poultry Association have bantams in their standards these do not usually have the same number of varieties as the Bantam Association. They have been standardized by the APA since its inception in 1874 and have continued to the present day.

The British and American standards are very similar and were formed from the same foundation—they did not have the same problems as the British Poultry Club in getting established, although standards had been drafted from 1864, as noted earlier. In fact, they had been in print in ***The Poultry Book*** (Tegetmeier) from an early date, the second edition being in 1873.

Whether the American *or* British standards was  the first to include the 100 points, suitably detailed, is not clear. Certainly , in Britain, W F Entwisle is credited with  creating the 100-point standard and this was taken up by Lewis Wright. However, the Official British standard appears to have been introduced after the Americans issued their first standards.  It matters not now because that is the general practice, although the method of *application and  interpretation* can be quite different.

**The Poultry Club Stand in 1949.**

# THE POULTRY CLUB

Mention should be made of the fine work done by the Poultry Club of Britain  which organizes the National Poultry Show, licences judges, and co-ordinates the standards so they can be published. Space does not permit giving full details on how it operates through a Council headed by a Chair Person and a President who is nominated and elected.

The show scene is the important side of the work done and it gives its support not only to the National Show, but also Championship shows throughout the country. The club or society must be affiliated to the Poultry Club and held under its rules, with Club judges (or specialists from clubs).

Special prize cards are awarded and if a bird wins three championship cards under separate judges the bird concerned can be named a 'Champion'. There are Gold, Silver and Bronze awards.

There are  Royal shows, Championship shows, and Regional shows, but there is some overlapping in these.

The supervision of judges and the results awarded is a heavy burden on the Club, and despite running special courses and tests, once the judges are in action, they are very much on their own. Later complaints from fanciers are difficult to deal with because often the condition of a bird on the day is the all-important factor. However, there are still birds being awarded *top* prizes with blatant faults; eg, a short-backed bird bird (a *standard* specification) given a top prize with a long back,  or a bird of the wrong colour also given a prize. This aspect requires to be controlled better.

## BREED CLUBS

The centre of the Fancy is the Poultry Club, but the main arteries of the system are the breed clubs, which look after the interests of a specific breed, issue a newsletter or booklet, and hold club shows.They can make or mar the whole system, but are obviously run by a dedicated secretary who does a great deal of work, often with limited resources.

# 3

# THE MAIN REQUIREMENTS: STANDARD BREEDS

**Rosecomb Bantam  Head with developed comb.**

These were one of the first to be shown.

### STANDARD BREEDS

A standard breed is one recognized by a breed club or Poultry Club or Association (USA) and which breeds consistently to the description laid down. Usually each breed has distinctive features (collectively known as *Type*, although this term is sometimes restricted to describe Shape only ), and there may be different varieties distinguished by plumage, comb, feathered legs or some other variable factor.

Proof of breeding true for a long period is normally required and this includes the absence of unwanted features such as the wrong type of comb, incorrect number of toes, feathered legs on a clean legged breed or other feature.

Although reference is made to "Pure Breeds" this simply means that they breed true, although strictly, there is no such thing as a *pure* breed because all come from the common source of the Jungle Fowl and have been developed over hundreds of years, although most of the breeds in their present form,  came into existence in Victorian times.  In any event, many of our modern standard breeds have been crossed many years  ago to produce distinct breeds with their own characteristics. Even old breeds such as Dorkings and Old English Game, which were present in England when the Romans came, have been modified.

# SELECTING THE BREED

There is a very wide choice available and therefore the would-be fancier must decide which breed is to be kept, bearing in mind:
1. **Hard or soft feathered.**
2. **Utility or fancy fowl.**
3. **Layer or table bird.**
4. **Bantams.**

## Understanding the Standard

### Written and Practical Standards

The *written* standard is the one issued by the breed club or poultry club. It is the definitive guide to what is expected of a particular breed. Generally it represents a reasonable measure against which to compare birds in the same class.

Nevertheless, this will only work provided the standard is up to date and is followed strictly by judges who should not indulge in selecting their pet likes or dislikes. Some like a particular colour, others like a very large bird, others a diminutive type, and so on. However, whatever the standard stipulates, should be the one taken.

Many years ago it was stated that judges rely on eye and experience to decide the winners and the standard is not usually consulted on the spot*. Sadly, this practice still goes on, which is fine if the standard is really known and understood by an officiating judge, but results awarded show that this is not always the case.

---

* **H Easom Smith,** *Modern Poultry Development,* **who suggested that many of the diehard fanciers did not own a copy of the Poultry Club Standard, never mind judging by them!!    He was a President of the Poultry Club.**

*The **practical standard;** ie, the* one applied by judges: may be a far cry from *the* one in *the* standards book. Examples of departure are as follows:

*1. Old English Game (large).* Should it be Oxford or Carlisle type and, if so, which one. Even there the matter is not straight forward. Many people do not understand the difference, believing that Oxford birds are rather coarse, narrow birds. The paintings by Herbert Atkinson show that there is a complete misunderstanding on what is an Oxford bird; many *modern* Oxfords are long and narrow and show signs of a cross with some other breed.

*2. OEG (bantams).* In the UK the tail of the bantam is now very sparse and this has been accepted by judges and the fancier, but the standard still calls for a large tail which is not accepted by judges.

*3. Indian Game (large)* Should be active birds, but far too many are heavy-weight giants not capable of breeding. The bantams are still active and continue to improve. However, they too need to be watched or they will become unhealthy like the massive large breed.

*4. Birds with large ear lobes.* Breeds such as Spanish, Rosecomb bantams, and Minorcas must excel in ear lobes or they will not win. The sizes now required are far beyond the expectations of the written standards.

*5. Laced Birds.* The various laced birds such as Laced Wyandottes, Indian Game. Barnevelders and Sebrights must have good, even lacing or they will not be given top prizes. Lacing is vital to their requirements and without it the breed in question is not conforming to type. However, the opposite may apply; birds with extremely good lacing may be given prizes, although they are imperfect in other features, such as having a faulty comb or long back in, say, Sebrights.

*6. Where colour is vital.* Some birds must be the exact colour or will usually (though not always) fail. Modern Game are an example when colour must be exact or they should not be given top prizes. Strangely, in the British Standards only 20 points are given for colour. This is also the case for Rhode Island Reds (25 points) yet without the deep chocolate colour no Rhode Island Red will win a top award—but this is not strictly a *true* red.

*The standards should be revised!*

*7. Special Feathering.* Breeds such as Silkies or Frizzles must have the maximum "silk" or curled feathers respectively or they fail. Silkies with hard feathering should be passed over.

*8. Excessive Feathering.* Utility type birds such as Wyandottes or Orpingtons, should not be too feathery or they lose shape and overall type. Crossing with other breeds may bring out some features, but exaggerate others. Thus in the case of Black Orpingtons, Cochin blood was introduced by Joseph Partington many years ago and some srains still show the effects with masses of superfluous feathers.

*9. Back Length.* Confusion with length of back— some breeds require to have very short backs (eg, OEG, Sebrights, Rosecombs) and others should have long backs (eg, Minorcas, Leghorns and Sussex) yet, blinded by other attributes, prizes are awarded even though the birds in question do not comply.

*10. Tails of the wrong type.* If a tail is too short, at the wrong angle, lacking sickle feathers when they should be present, or some other incorrect type of tail, a particular bird may be affected to the extent that it is completely the wrong *type.* However, fanciers must appreciate the term is being used in a way which indicates shape *or other attributes or features which make up the characteristics of a breed.*

Other examples could be quoted, but the message is to develop birds which have all the required features in a co-ordinated fashion, not being biased in one particular way, Bantams in particular should be quite *symmetrical* and often it is lack of balance, seen in many breeds, and especially OEG and Rosecombs, that a bird fails.

• • • • • • • • • • • • • • • • • • • • • • • • • • • • • • • • • • • • • • • •

Indicates *incorrect carriage,* poor tail angle and sparse hackle

V-Shaped Back (instead of U-shape)

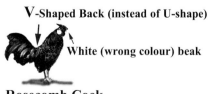

White (wrong colour) beak

**EXAMPLE OF FAULTS**

**Rosecomb Cock**

# THE KEY FACTORS

When getting ready to enter birds in a show it will be necessary to study the standards and decide which "key factors" are vital to winning; without this recognition an exhibit is unlikely to be in the awards.

A clue to the key factors can be obtained from studying the official standards. In some cases a feature will stand out immediately and will probably be given a high mark in the points scheme. In other cases, although not given formal recognition, the feature in question will be foremost in the mind of the judge and without its presence there is little hope of winning.

**Thus in Old English Game there are three main requirements: *shape; condition* and *good legs* and *feet*. A bird which is narrow, or out of condition or is duck-footed will stand no chance and should not be exhibited.**

**EXAMPLES OF KEY FACTORS (not all breeds listed)**

|           *Breed*          |      *Main or KEY FACTORS*          |
|----------------------------|-------------------------------------|
| **Ancona:**                | Shape; Colour and Tipping 45; Head 20 = **65 points** |
| **Andalusian:**            | Colour and Lacing 50; Head 25 = **75 points** |
| **Aseel:**                 | Head and Type 45; Condition 20 = **65 points** |
| **Australorp**             | Type 35; Head 25; Free from Coarseness 15 = **75 points** |
| **Barnevelder**            | Type and Colour 55: Texture 15 = **65 points** |

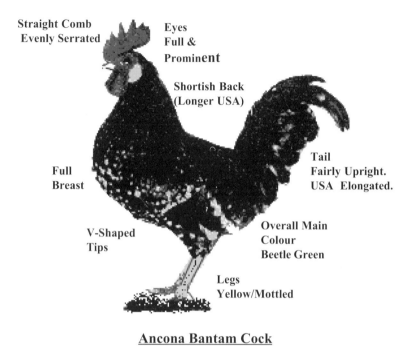

Straight Comb
Evenly Serrated

Eyes
Full &
Prominent

Shortish Back
(Longer USA)

Full
Breast

Tail
Fairly Upright.
USA  Elongated.

V-Shaped
Tips

Overall Main
Colour
Beetle Green

Legs
Yellow/Mottled

### Ancona Bantam Cock

## The Essentials for the Ancona

The fancier must be able to analyse the Key Factors for his or her breed and make sure they are present in the birds to be shown

See the Table for the Ancona and note that colour and tipping make up the biggest number of points, but do not neglect the other factors shown above.

• • • • • • • • • • • • • • • • • • • • • • • • • • • • • • • • • • • •

NOTE: For a detailed examination see
*The Ancona Fowl,* J Batty.

**Brahma:**                          Type, Size and Head 55;
                                     Colour 40 = **95 points**

**Bresse:**                          Type and Head 45;
                                     Colour 15 = **60 points**

**Campine:**                         Colour and Markings 55;
                                     Head 15 = **70 points**

**Cochin:**                          Feathering 35; Colour 20;
                                     Size 15 = **70 points**

**Croad Langshan:**                  Type and Body 50; Plum -
                                     age   25 = **75 points**

**Dorking:**                         **(Varies with colour)** —
                                     Size 15-28; Colour12-24;Type
                                     12-20  = **maximum 72 points**

**Faverolles:**                      Utility and Type 50;
                                     Colour 20; Beard 15
                                     **= 85 points**

**Frizzle:**                         Type and Colour 50;
                                     Curl 30 = **80 points**

**Hamburgh:**                        **(Varies)** —Head 20-45;
                                     Colour  and Markings 25-60—
                                     **Total points vary.**

**Indian Game:**                     Type and Colour 53; Head 17
                                     = **70   points**

Comb with 5 or 6 spikes
Beak Longish;
Head small, set well back.

U-Shaped at tail & shoulders; back medium set midway in body.
Legs longish to fit body;
feathered outer side.
*Note: Stds state medium legs, but they appear to be longish.*

Tail high but not squirrel tailed.

Breast to be full and broad.

Colour: Beetle green/black
No purple or blue tinges.

## Croad Langshan Cock & Hen (Silhouettes)
**Ideals painted by Ernest Wippell the poultry artist.
The American standards are rather different—more like the Modern Langshan which has longer legs.**

**Japanese Bantams:**                Type and Size  25-35;
                                     Plumage 15-30 = **65 points**


**Leghorn:**                         (Varies) Type and Colour 40;Size
                                     and Symmetry 30 = **70 points**


**Modern Game:**                     Type and Style 30; Colour 20 =
                                                         **50  points**


**Modern Langshan:**                 Type and Carriage 35;
                                     Colour 20 = **55 points**


**New Hampshire Red:**               Type and Carriage 25;
                                     Colour 20; Dual
                                     Purpose 15 = **60 points**


**North Holland Blue:**              Table and Egg Merits 40;
                                     Colour 20 = **60 points**


**Old English Game:**                Body, Carriage and Han-
                                     dling 44; Legs and Feet 18;
                                                         = **62 points**


**Old English Pheasant Fowl:**       Head 25; Type 20; Colour 35
                                                 = **80 points**

Close Dubbing on Cock

Short Hackle

Broad Tapering to Back (Narrow)

Fine Comb

Whip Tail

Good Shoulders

Sloping Flat Back

Plenty of 'Lift'

Prominent Breast

Long Legs Flat Toes

Elegant and well trained

No Fluff at Abdomen

### Modern Game Bantams

Elegant 'Dandies' developed for showing.
Modern Game are tall and the Bantam variety must be elegant with a long reach.
Colours must be exactly as specified in the standard.
Hard feathering and exact colouring are essential.

See *Understanding Modern Game*, Bleazard & Batty for full details. Dubbing, the trimming of the comb of the male bird, is essential, and fanciers should seek advice from an experienced breeder. Also see *Understanding Old English Game,* J Batty, where the technique is explained.

**Orpington:**          (Varies with colour) - Type and Size 40-45; Colour and Plumage 10-25 = **maximum 70 points.** **Note: Black**—Head 25

**Pekin Bantams:**          Colour and Markings 20; Feathering **25 = 45 points**

**Plymouth Rock:**          (Varies) Type 30; Colour and Markings 30-35 **= maximum 60 points**

**Poland:**          Head, Breast, etc 40-45; Colour and Markings 30 = **maxmum 75  points**

**Redcap:**          Head 45; Colour 25 **= 70 points**

**Rhode Island Red:**          Shape 30; Colour and Quality 35 **= 65 points**

**Rosecomb Bantams:**          Head 35 (comb 20, ear lobes15);Type 15: Tail 15: **=  65 points**

**Scots Dumpies:**          Type 40; Size 20  **= 60 points**

**Scots Greys:**          Colour and Markings 50: Size 15 **= 65 points**

**The Pekin Bantam**
These are purely show birds which have been developed to a very
high standard over the last decade or so.

**Sebright:**                Colour and Lacing 40; Type 20
                            = **60 points**

**Silkie:**                  Head 30; Plumage 30; Type 20
                            = **80 points**

**Spanish:**                 Face and Wattles 50; Type and
                            Size 30 = **80 points**

**Sultan:**                  Head, Crest, Beard, etc, 35;
                            Colour 15;    Legs 15
                            = **65 points**

**Sumatra Game:**            Type 20; Head 20; Colour 15;
                            Feathers 15  = **70 points**

**Sussex:**                  Type 25; Size 20; Colour 20
                            = **65 points**

**Welsummer:**               Type 20; Utility 30; Colour
                            20 = **70 points**

**Wyandotte:**               (Varies between colours and
                            male and female) - Colour 15-
                            70; Type 25 - **No. of points
                            varies**

**Yokohama:**                Plumage 45; Type 25
                            = **70 points**

**The Jaunty Sebrights**
Far too many have long backs

**Sumatra**
Must have very glossy feathers of black with considerable green sheen, and a flowing tail.

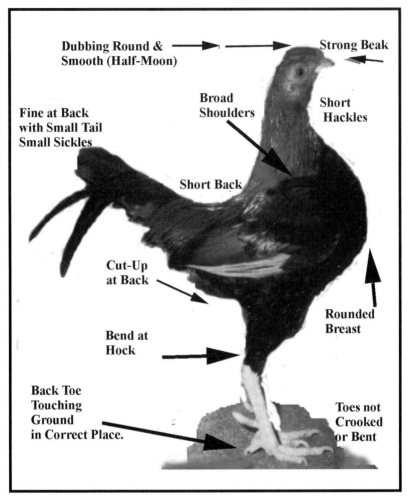

**Dubbing Round &** ➝ ──── ➝ **Strong Beak**
**Smooth (Half-Moon)**

**Broad**
**Shoulders**

**Short**
**Hackles**

**Fine at Back**
**with Small Tail**
**Small Sickles**

**Short Back**

**Cut-Up**
**at Back**

**Rounded**
**Breast**

**Bend at**
**Hock**

**Back Toe**
**Touching**
**Ground**
**in Correct Place.**

**Toes not**
**Crooked**
**or Bent**

### Top Prize Winner OEG Bantam Cock
### (Trevor E Thompson)

See the various requirements and compare with the Large Game opposite.
This is a Black Red so the colour must also comply with the Colour
Standard.

Full
Sickles Strong Tail
Nicely Angled.

Medium Dubbing

Full
yet Short
Hackle
(not like
Modern
Game).

Strong
Beak

Very
Short

Broad
Shoulders

Muscular
Thighs

Close
Heeled
Essential

Fine
Spurs

Full &
Curved
Breast

Feet Flat
to
Ground.
Not Duck-
Footed.

### The Ideal Old English Game Cock

Drawn by the 'Master' himself (Herbert Atkinson) to show how a good balanced Game Fowl should appear. Moreover, this is the Oxford type and a far cry from the mangy, narrow birds now being bred by some of the so-called Oxford supporters.

For the non-Game fancier it should be noted that Herbert Atkinson was the leader of the Oxford Fowl Club which still exists and holds shows. He painted many fine portraits of winning Game fowl and with his friend John Harris encouraged the breeding of the old type of fighting Game. The above drawing was done by him to illustrate his ideal cock.

*NOTE: Learn to analyse the key factors and then see how far these fall short of the Ideal.*

Cradle-Type
Rose Comb

Cushion
&
Tail
Medium

Short Back

Full
Breast
Body
Deep
&
Round

Abdomen
Not Low
or Fluffy

Legs
Visible

**Wyandotte Cockerel Champion**
British exhibits in bantams are usually much too feathery
In USA tail at an angle (40 degrees)—more sloping.
Colour very important, including legs, beak and skin.

# 4

# THE TYPE

*Fix the Standard Shape in the Mind*

TYPE in the British standards is used loosely to mean all kinds of things and, as a result there is much confusion. In the USA  the American Standards tend to steer away from the use of  the term, and, instead, detail each attribute into Shape, Head, Neck, Back, Tail, wings, Breast, Body & Fluff,  Legs & Toes.

### Sebright Bantam Top Winner

This bird is in very good condition and the lacing is first class. However, it suffers from a major fault; namely, a long back. Yet it was placed as one of the best exhibits in a major show.

This error in judging occurs quite frequently. The judge spots excellent features such as the lacing (Sebrights) or the comb and wattles (Rosecombs) and ignores the essential requirement of the short back.

For a detailed analysis see *The Sebright Bantam*, J Batty.

# ANALYSIS OF KEY FACTORS
## Type

This is the description used to denote the outward shape, including the **essential body outline;** eg circle, ovoid, squarish, rectangle. Each breed has an expected shape and therefore this must be recognised before any attempt is made to determine likely winners. It also implies "balance" or symmetry and often includes the head description; eg small, large, broad etc. Most breeds have *Type* as the key factor.

It is probably the most misused word in Poultry Circles, meaning so many things to different breeds and as used by different people.

Before considering the show requirements in detail it is necessary to look at the *overall conformation* of a breed. often referred to as Type. This has been defined by different authors as follows:

**1. The type, or shape, of a bird is the good or bad resemblance to its breed.** *(Dictionary of Poultry,* **D F Suttie, 1931)**

**2. Mould or Shape** *(British Poultry Standards, 1997 )*

**3. The general shape and form, common to all members of a breed resulting from breeding to an Ideal shape and size as set forth in the Standard of Perfection.** *(American Standard of Perfection)*

**4. Bantam Standard has its own type—body shape, tail development and angle, ear lobe eolour and shape, eye eolour, shank eolour, feather quality and many other points. (** *Bantam Breeding & Genetics,* **Fred P Jeffrey, Hindhead, 1977 ).**

This approach by Jeffrey views TYPE in a much wider sense than that admitted by the *Standards* and there is little doubt that this is the correct approach. Shape alone is not good enough because a bird can have the correct body shape. but other features which are out of line with the rest of the standard. Breed characteristics, including weight are also important.

George R Scott, a "rebel" of the Poultry Fancy, went into more detail and was more positive in exposing the fallacy of:

Type *equals* Shape: *(The Truth About Poultry,* London, nd). For instance, the word " type " is employed in the Poultry Fancy with a carelessness that staggers comprehension. The *type* of a breed has, in some incomprehensible and fantastic way, grown in the minds of the vast majority to indicate precisely and exclusively the *shape* of that breed. If this were all and the word type itself were dropped completely out of poultry nomenclature it would not matter a great deal. But type and shape are treated as synonyms and used alternatively with freedom and gusto !

Examples of the confusion resulting from the loose use of type and shape, as applied to fowls, abound in their thousands in poultry books and in the press generally. Lewis Wright continually errs, in one paragraph employing type correctly and in another giving to it an entirely different meaning. The examples given below I have taken at random from the latest edition of Wright's *Book of Poultry.* The contradictory meanings given to the word type will be readily apparent. The italics are mine.

Plymouth Rocks, Chapter XIX p 308, "The American Barred Rock differs from the *English type perceptibly in shape."*

Chapter XXXI, French Breeds, p 468 "The type of Houdan bred in America *differs* somewhat from the English. From all the descriptions we have seen, the comb appears to be preferred of a two-horned rather than leaf character, and the plumage darker than in England."

Chapter XXXIII, Unclassed Breeds of Poultry, p. 498. " While at a first glance the Lakenvelder gives one the idea of *Leghorn Type,* closer scrutiny soon makes it clear that it truly belongs to the Braekel or Hamburgh family. Its *different size,* its dark legs, and its carriage resemble that class of fowl, and its small eggs and unsuitableness for close confinement show the same relationship."

**Black Spanish Fowl**

Correct shape is important, but there are many other factors to consider in deciding whether a bird complies with the Standard. As noted in the preceding chapter *Face & Wattle* come to 50 points and *Size* 30 points. The overall *shape*, nonetheless, is still important and birds which do come near the standard , even with perfect face and wattles, should not win.

## TRUE  MEANING  OF  *TYPE*

From what has been stated,  the term 'Type' is used loosely to mean many things. Moreover, the usage is quite inconsistent; to one it means one thing, to another something different.Although this is the case, The British Poultry Club Standards states: *Mould or shape*, and also refers to 'symmetry' which is the correct balancing of the different parts. Presumably this also refers to the shape.

The American Standards prefer to use headings of requirements, Shape being one of them. For them TYPE means the general shape common to members of the specific breed, and specified as an *Ideal.*

Used in a broad sense *type* means a collection of attributes which go to make the breed, shape being only one, but without the correct shape there can be no compliance with the standard.

In this chapter the meaning of Shape is considered.

### Shape

Shape, along with the feathering, determines the breed of bird.  From a brief viewing an experienced poultry breeder or fancier can see what breed is being dealt with. However, this recognition is not always easy or straight forward because so many breeds are similar.

Many related breeds have a similar shape so the so-called Mediterranean breeds have a specific shape which is recognizable . This group includes Anconas, Andalusians, Leghorns, and Minorcas. The body is fairly horizontal, the tail is large and the legs are visible. Yet this description is *similar* to some other breeds such as Old English Game, Campines, Hamburghs, Old English Pheasant Fowl and others. Only by looking at other features as well and the details of the shape will it be possible to be exact.

Some have long backs, eg; Mediterranean breeds, whereas others must have short backs. The heavy breeds usually have broad breasts which are rounded and broad. There are some of these which are heavily feathered which has underneath the soft feathers or fluff. This also affects the shape, some birds being quite 'bulky'.

**A Variety of Breeds**
Note the differences even in such a small number.

**Minorca Female
 Tail longish.
'Gamey' Looking.
Sometimes the shape
is confused with the
Andalusian Male.**

Note: to complicate matters we see *variations* in tail and general shape, which still comply with the standard description because some latitude must be allowed.

**Ancona Female
Shortish Tail**

**Silhouettes of Shape**

**Andalusian**
**Male**
**Full tail.**
**See Ancona**
<u>**Opposite**</u>

**British Leghorn (Male)**
**Tail moderate at 45$^0$ angle.**
**Legs longish.**

**Silhouettes of Shape**

**Shape of Body**

<u>Ancona</u>
Left:  British
Right: American

### Silhouettes

Andalusians

Leghorns

Minorcas

Spanish

Sicilian Buttercup

## Mediterranean Breeds
These are all light breeds which lay white eggs and do not usually come
broody. The body is oval shape rather like an egg.

Campines which have oval
bodies, but fairly upright.

Scots Greys which have a similar
body and carriage to Leghorn.

Bresse a French breed
Appears to be closely related
to Leghorn.

Redcaps —similar to
Mediterranean breeds
Emphasis is on v. large comb.

Silver Spangled Hamburgh
Follows the Leghorn in body
but comb and tail different

Old English Pheasant Fowl
Related to Redcap and Hamburghs.

**Breeds similar to Leghorns in having oval bodies.**

Faverolles: Note essentials of
muffles, feathered legs and
fifth toe.

Orpingtons

Cochin
Note feathered legs
Single Comb

Brahma Cock
Note Pea Comb
Not as Rounded as Cochin
Nor as loose feathered.

Silkies—"Silk in abundance"
Note very short back—vital!

Black Rocks

Wyandotte "A bird of Curves"

New Hampshire Reds
Note similarity to RIR
but higher tail and rounder
body.

## Round or Globular Shapes or Elongated Spheres

**Rhode Island Reds Silhouette
Purports to be Brick Shaped.**

This was the Ideal drawn by F J Chatterton the Poultry artist (1920s), but these days the body tends to look longer and not so deep.

**Double Laced Barnevelder
Note the similarity to the RIR, but not as rectangular**

**Indian Game Cock (Ideal)
This should have a
'blocky' squarish body.
Many heavy weights are
too lethargic and legs too
short, so there are breathing
problems.
The modern birds of the
English stamp have a more
upright and shorter tail.
USA = Cornish**

## Unusual Shapes

# Breeds of Similar Shapes

In the past advantage has been taken of breeds which are similar. Apparently a breed now extinct, called the "Albion" was used to represent White Sussex and Orpingtons, and there may have been some involvement by Dorking breeders.

Judges and fanciers must be aware of the similarities which exist or substitutions may occur.

With some, although having a shape which is almost identical, there may be differences which can help to distinguish two breeds. In the example opposite,  the distinguishing features are indicated.

Wyandottes have a **cradle-shape** comb so it should be possible to spot any breed which is supposed to have a single comb, like the Sussex, and immediately recognize the fault. In case you think this is simply an exercise to stretch the imagination, remember that many of the standard heavy breeds were made up of a number of other breeds, before becoming 'stable'. However, occasionally the features of an ancestor may suddenly appear and mar the breed concerned.

The sheer size of a bird may give some indication of the breed, but this rule is not infallible. Except in bantams and Old English Game the tendency is for the larger birds to win anyway, YET BIRDS WHICH ARE EXCESSIVELY LARGE DO NOT COMPLY WITH ONE OF THE BREED CHARACTERISTICS; ie, SIZE. and should be penalized.

## A PRACTICAL EXERCISE

*A useful and interesting exercise is to list  similar breeds and specify which features are the same and which are different. This enables the fancier and would-be judge to analyse the principal factors and apply the knowledge in improving a strain.*

# Breeds that Look Alike.

**POINTS OF DIFFERENCE**

**LIGHT SUSSEX** | **COLUMBIAN WYANDOTTE**

Sussex has white Legs & Single Comb.
COLUMBIAN WYANDOTTE has yellow Legs Rose Comb & Cobbier Shape.

**WHITE LEGHORN** | **WHITE LA BRESSE**

LEGHORN has yellow Legs.

LA BRESSE has Blue Legs.

**SPECKLED SUSSEX** | **JUBILEE ORPINGTON**

SUSSEX is longer in the Body.

ORPINGTON is deeper.

**RED SUSSEX** | **RHODE ISLAND RED**

SUSSEX has White Legs and Slate under colour.

RHODE ISLAND RED has Yellow Legs & Sound Red undercolour.

R.D.FARNIE

*See opposite*

## Malays
**Must be tall with cruel expression, pale eyes and very tight feathering.**

---

## Japanese Shamos (Red-hackled)
**Note the very drooping tail.**

Tails not as drooping
as on  Large Shamo,
although
do on some varieties
of
Shamo bantams.

Shamo Bantams (Japanese)
## Breeds with very Sloping Carriage

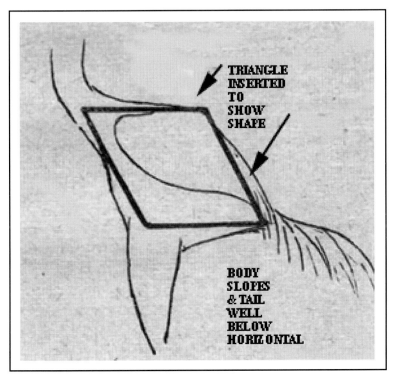

TRIANGLE
INSERTED
TO
SHOW
SHAPE

BODY
SLOPES
& TAIL
WELL
BELOW
HORIZONTAL

## Malay Shape

The sloping body and tail which also slopes towards the ground is typical of many Asian breeds and any failure to achieve this ideal, spoils the overall requirement.

**Aseel: note the below horizontal tail. Feathering very close.**

Modern Game
Birchen Cock
Related to Malays,
hence sloping body.
Whip tail, snakey neck
and perfect feathering
and colours essential.

All Game Must have tight
(hard) feathering, as well
as flatbacks, wide
shoulders and perfect legs.

This OEG bantam
is lacking balance
(poor tail). Front
too prominent.
This type should
be discouraged or
tail will disappear.

OEG Bantam (Elegant)
Type favoured 1950-60

OEG Bantam
Type in 1997 British Standards

**Hard feathered breeds (Game)**

## SUMMARY

The basic shape of a bird is a vital part of the breed requirement. If there is any radical variation then it is not the correct form or the bird in question is a cross or is reverting back to one of the original breeds used in forming the breed under scrutiny.

Shape alone is not sufficient evidence of a breed's identity because other factors determine how the shape appears on the living bird. Factors which could affect the position are:

**1. Tail and its angle.**

**2. Legs and whether straight or bent at the hock and to what extent.**

**3. Carriage or posture. Some birds stand upright with very prominent breasts, whereas others have a fairly horizontal carriage.**

**4. Size and position of head.**

**5. Plumage and whether 'Hard' or 'Soft' feathered. These terms are misleading because there are varying degrees; how can we compare, say, a Leghorn, with the heavily feathered Cochin, yet they are both soft feathered. Sensibly, in the USA the term *soft feathered* is avoided in the *Terminology*. What is needed is a classification which gives a range of types of feathering and this would eliminate the profusely feathering appearing in what should be medium feathered breeds.**

A change in one would affect the appearance of a bird so it would have to be penalized or even missed from the judging.

## Types

*Rounded Body*

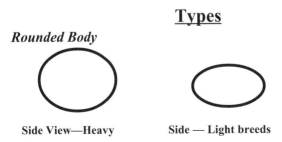

Side View—Heavy            Side — Light breeds

Tail

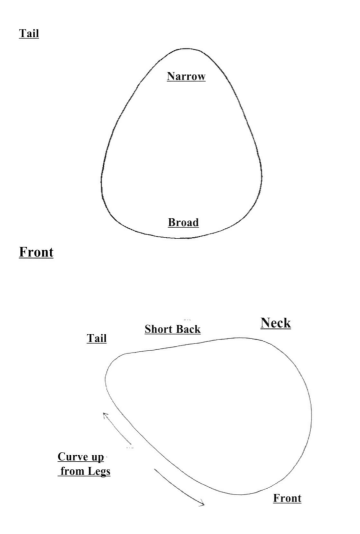

Front

**Essentials of Old English Game and other Short Backed Birds**

Note: Leghorns and similar breeds discussed earlier, will have a similar shape, but will be slimmer and longer in the back.

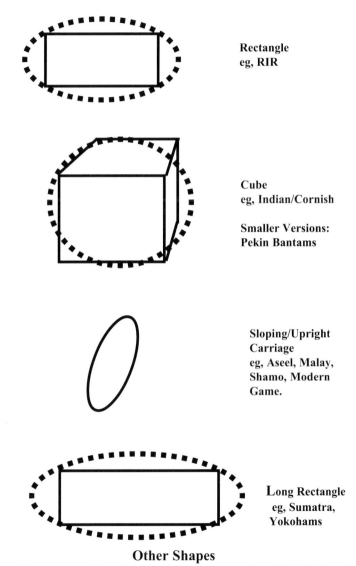

Rectangle
eg, RIR

Cube
eg, Indian/Cornish

Smaller Versions:
Pekin Bantams

Sloping/Upright
Carriage
eg, Aseel, Malay,
Shamo, Modern
Game.

Long Rectangle
eg, Sumatra,
Yokohams

## Other Shapes

These shapes are purely notional—no bird is square shaped, but the breeder must imagine the shape *fitting within* the rounded body.

# BODY FAULTS

The faults which may be found are quite varied and therefore it is impossible to cover all possibilities. However, general references can be made and these should be applied:

**1. Wrong Size**

**2. Body too deep, too long, or too short as defined in the Poultry Standard for the breed concerned.**

**3. Feathering not in accordance with the standard; many breeds have lost the utility aspects for which they were developed and this affects the shape.**

## EXAMPLES

**Orpington (Too Cochiny)**

**Rhode Island Red (Body too deep)**

**Minorca with poor carriage.**

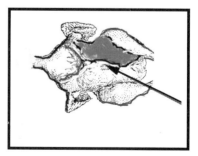

**Bent Breast Bone (Bent Keel).**

# 5

# POULTRY
# COMBS

**Sicilian Buttercup Comb**
**Said to mean the *Sacred Cup of Riches*, the bird**
**originally being used for sacrifices in its native Sicily**

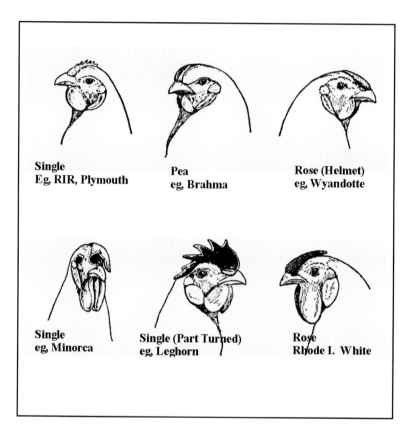

## Ideal Types of Combs (Females)

These are based on USA bred birds, but would also apply in Britain.

## TYPES OF COMB

There are many types of comb and some breeds are found with Single comb *or* Rose. Moreover, with the latter, the combs appear in different forms so it is to be found with quite distinct features; thus, Derbyshire Redcaps have a very wide comb which is quite distinctive and others have different types of leaders (spikes).

The most common type is the single comb and this consists of a number of spikes or points which vary in numbers according to the breed. Sometimes a Standard specifies the number of points, but at other times does not give the exact number. Thus in the American standard the comb of the Orpington is stated to have 5 points, but the British does not specify. However, it is obvious that a comb should be balanced and any number over six is likely to be excessive and less than five will appear out of balance.

The comb of the male is larger than the female and, in both, is brighter when the birds are in top condition. Any hen with a dull comb is unlikely to be laying and a hen looks best with a vitally bright comb. However, when showing, attempts may be made to delay laying by moving birds into different accommodation or reducing the hours of lighting. Once a hen starts to lay there will be a loss of condition and certain breeds, such as Old English Game, may be penalised because the abdomen is low, caused by laying.

Very often OEG breeders stick to mixed corn feeding so that hens do not come soft in the feather and lose the streamlining cut up at the back, so essential in the correctly shaped bird. The intention is to keep the hen in show condition, but with the minimum of egg laying. However, the author has experimented with a *corn-only* feed and, alternatively, layers' pellets, and has found that the corn diet alone causes feathers to be quite brittle, which break easily.

## *COMB VARIATIONS*

The variations in the combs of fowls are considerable. As will be evident there are differences in size and other detail even though many are similar. Sir Edward Brown classified combs as follows:*

**1. Rose Comb**, in which the leader or spike behind *follows the line of neck*. As is usual in all combs of this nature there is a considerable number of what are called points, that is, more or less regular growths.

 **2. Triple or Pea Comb,** giving the appearance of three distinct fleshy ridges side by side, the centre being the highest.

**3. Rose Comb,** in which the leader is carried straight behind and *above the line of neck.*

**4. Walnut Comb,** resembling a half walnut on top of the skull

**5. Redcap Comb,** very large and heavy, often coarse, and with a very small leader.

**6. Mulberry Comb (or Cushion Comb)** carried in front, deep purple in colour, eg; Silkie.

**7. Small Single Comb,** as found on heavy-bodied breeds.

**8. Large Single Comb,** found on light-bodied breeds, usually following the line of neck behind, and falling over to one side in hens. In Single combed fowls there is a tendency to growths known as *side sprigs,* which are objectionable.

**9. Buttercup Comb,** forming a complete cup without any growth in the centre. This is also known as a **Cup Comb** and is capable of holding water.

---

*Poultry Breeding and Production* , London, 1929

**10. Small Rose Comb**, fine in points, and with straight leader.

**11. Strawberry or Butterfly Comb** with a protuberance in the centre.

**I2. Horned Comb,** with sharp spikes rising from head.

**I3. Small Single Comb** on hens of heavy breeds.

**14. Large Single Comb** on hens of light breeds which are heavy layers.

**15. Single Comb** slightly carried on one side.

These combs are shown overleaf and are the work of Ernest Wippell. Number 2 is misleading because the centre ridge should be higher than the remainder; in the recent British Poultry Standards this has been corrected to show the centre ridge clearly.

The term 'Mulberry Comb' is not a proper description because this relates to the colour rather than the shape. There are others with dark combs such as Sebright bantams.

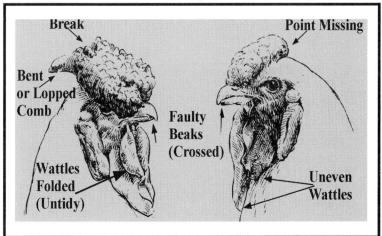

**Faults in Rose Combed Birds**
*(After J H Robinson)*

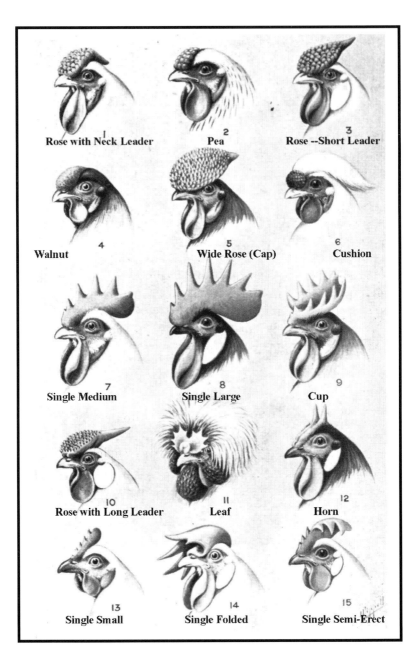

# A Guide To Drawings Opposite

**1. Rose Comb:** leader follows the line of neck. The comb is full of points or " Work " and should not obstruct the sight of either eye.

**2. Triple or Pea Comb.** It will be noticed that there is no leader to a pea comb. It is like three combs side-by-side, *the centre being the highest.*

**3. Rose Comb.** In this case the leader must be straight in line with the top of the comb, and well up from the neck.

**4. Walnut Comb.** Like a half walnut placed on the head.

**5. Redcap Comb,** the largest of the rose comb series. Cock's comb sometimes measures 5 by 4 inches (12.5cm x 10cm), the points should be all up to the same level; comb, free from "pits" should sit squarely on the head.

**6. Mulberry Comb (or Cushion Comb)**, a good description for colour, as this comb is often a deep Purple colour. However, the modern term is "Cushion Comb" which describes the form better.

**7. Single Comb**, heavy breeds must he upright, clean in serrations, and *free from budding side sprigs.*

**8. Single Comb,** light breeds, larger than comb in heavy breeds, the spikes should be wedge-shaped and not too numerous.

**9. Buttercup Comb,** male. the name implies a "cup" comb, and a perfect comb should hold water, and be free from growths in centre.

**10. Rose Comb,** distinguished by its very long straight leader, and full fine works.

**11. Butterfly Comb** male— certainly resembles the opened wings of a butterfly should be evenly matched and well spread.

**12. Horned Comb,** just two plain upright spikes.

**13. Single Comb,** female sitting breed, which is small and upright.

**14. Single Comb,** non-sitting breed, female, falls first to one side, and then completely over to the other.

**15. Single Comb,** semi- or half over, i.e., has no fold, peculiar to some light breeds.

**Six-Pointer Dorking Comb**

**Five-Pointer Orpington**

## Heavy Breed Cocks: Medium Combs

**Minorca Cock**

**Leghorn Cock**

**Five Serrations Preferred (UK)**
**USA Six Points Preferred**

**USA MEDIUM Five Pointer**
**UK  Moderately Large**

## Light Breed: Single Combs

The aim is to pick a comb of the correct size with the points perfectly
pointed and evenly balanced.  The shape and position are of great
importance.

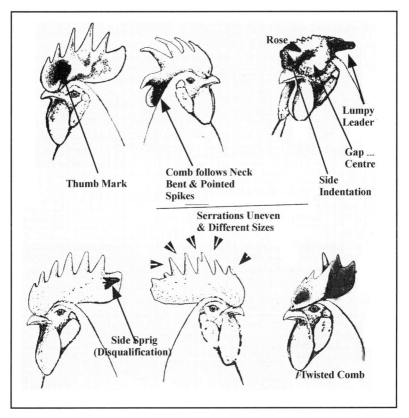

**Comb Faults and Defects**
*(After Slocum)*

### OPPOSITE  Single Combs.

Examples of large, medium and small combs are given opposite. It will be noted that large combs are few in number, most being medium. Accordingly, if very large combs are present the standard should be checked very carefully.Generally, with single combs 5 points are  preferred, but with Minorcas 6 points. All should be smooth without coarseness.

## SINGLE-COMBED BREEDS—MOST USUAL COMB FORM

Ancona
Andalusian
Barnevelder
Bresse
Campine
Castillian
Cochin
Croad Langshan
Dorking (except white)
Faverolles
Frizzle
Game —OEG and Modern
Jersey Giants
Lakenvelder
Leghorn
Langshan —Croad & Modern
Malines
Marans
Marsh Daisy
Minorca (Also Medium Rose)
New Hampshire Red
Norfolk Grey
North Holland Blue
Orpington   (Black large also Rose)
Plymouth Rock
Rhode Island Red (Also Rose)
Rumpless
Scots Dumpy
Scots Grey
Spanish
Sussex
Transylvanian Naked Neck
Vorverk
Welsummer
Yokohama

### MEDIUM SINGLE
*Examples*
Ancona
Barnevelder
Marans
New Hampshire Red
Rhode Island Red
Sussex
Welsummer

## Large combs
Jersey Giants
Leghorn
Minorca

## Small Combs
Cochin
Modern Langshan
Orpington
Spanish

**ROSE COMB**
Dominique—spike slightly
up turned.
Dorking (white)—broadish
 with upturned spike.
Hamburgh — medium with longish spike coming to a point & straight.
Marsh Daisy— straight short spike (not too high).
Old English Pheasant Fowl—spike slightly downwards.
Redcap— Very Broad comb with negligible spike.
Rhode Island Red and RIR White—small spike.
Rosecomb Bantam— spike largish extending from well developed comb with point.
Wyandotte—helmet or cradle comb with spike following line of neck.

**PEA COMB (Triple with middle row higher)**
Araucana
Aseel
Brahma
Buckeye
Cornish (USA)
Indian
Ixworth
Orloff
Phoenix
Shamo
Sumatra

**LEAF COMB**
Houdan

**SPIKE COMB (HORNS)**
 Crevecoeur
 La Fleche
 Poland
 Sultan

# CUP COMB
Sicilian Buttercup
Sicilian Flowerbird

Cup Comb— see page 75.

WALNUT/ STRAWBERRY
Malay
Kraienkoppe
Orloff


CUSHION
Chantecler
Silkie— must be neat and preferably purple in colour on
the male.
Lumpy, ugly combs should be penalized.


## TRUE BANTAMS

Mention must be made of the natural or *True Bantams* which
do not have an equivalent large variety. These are:

Belgian Bantams:

Barbu D'Anvers—Rose with spike curving downwards
following neck.

Barbu D'Uccle—Single and smallish.

Barbu De Watermael—Rose, medium, with 3 small
leaders.

Booted—single of medium height.

Dutch—single, tending to be large for size of bird.

Japanese—single, very high.

Nankin—normally single and largish extending back.

Pekin—supposed to be small, but in relation to bird are large
and single.

Rosecomb—Rose tending to be long with pointed spike rising
slightly.

Sebright—Rose tending to be long with pointed spike upturning
slightly.

Tuzo—pea or walnut.


In true bantams, since they are purely show birds, the comb
should be exactly to the specification in the standard.

**More Details of Combs**

## WATTLES

An  adjunct of the comb, hanging below the beak, are two fleshy rounded pieces,which are known as **wattles**. They should be of equal size and in accordance with the standard. Thus many breeds, such as Rhode Island Reds and Plymouth Rocks  have medium size wattles and others are large— ;eg, the Mediterranean breeds such as Minorcas or Leghorns. The Aseel should have no wattles and some breeds very little.

Faults are fairly numerous and include black or purple marks, tears, wattles of different sizes or of the wrong shape, and rough-ness or excessive wrinkles.

## LOBES

Lobes should be the correct shape and colour. If white is specified then red or other colours must be penalized. Alternatively, where red lobes are the standard any white should constitute a fault.

The shape is critical whether round or almond or other vari-ation. The Minorca should be elongated and almond shaped, but often are round in bantams because of Rosecomb blood.

One of the criticisms of show birds has been the attempt to achieve a very large size in lobes. This applies to the Rosecomb bantam, Minorca, Old English Pheasant Fowl, Leghorns, Hamburghs and Dutch bantams. Quality rather than quantity should be the aim.

**Minorca Cock Showing Correct, Elongated Lobe.**

# 6

# TAILS

**Orpington Male**  **Female**

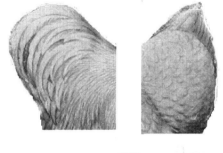

**British
Minorca
Cock**

*Tails grow in many sizes and varieties*

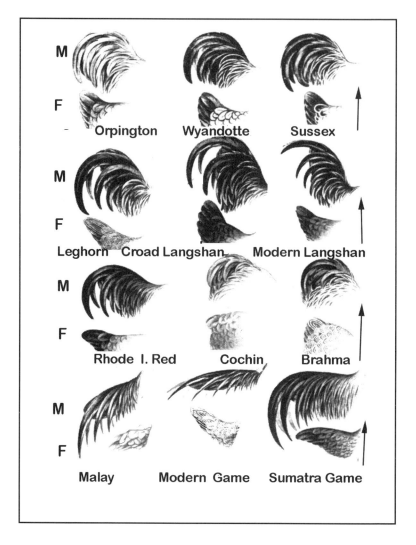

**Poultry Tails as drawn by Ernest Wippell**
This artist specialized in poultry *ideals* and produced many illustrations
which have been adapted and used by authors and poultry societies.

### Tails In Males and Females —Drawings Opposite.

The tails of poultry vary in characteristics; those shown are the males in the top row, and the female tails below. Perhaps it might seem of little importance, but, to the contrary, often the tail and its angle are dominant factors in all breeds.

The tails of heavy breeds, such as the Orpington, Wyandotte, and the Sussex, are close set, the main sickle feathers following closely the form of the tail; this feature is seen in the extreme in the very heavy breeds like the Cochin and Brahma.

The more active breeds show more openness and jauntiness in their tail carriage and more daylight can be seen between the pairs of sickles. The Leghorn may be taken as a type of the non-sitters, with its flowing sickles in the male, and prominent or whip tail in the female, carried either at an angle of 45 degrees or perpendicular according to the dictates of utility or exhibition standards.

The R. I. Red has a characteristic, almost horizontal tail carriage, the nearest approach being the tail carriage of the Buff and Barred Rock. Here tail carriage is very important.

The Malay represents the lowest tail carriage of any variety, as the downward curve is one of its standard points.

The " whipped " tail of the Modern Game is a distinct phase of tail carriage, the feathers being shorter and much narrower than the feathers of other breeds.

The flowing lines of the Sumatra tail are amazing but far from the wonderful tail of the Yokohama or Japanese Long Tail— here length and breadth are desirable and, as the illustration portrays, there is a tendency to "sickle" in the feathers of the female, this tendency being the basis of selection when mating up for length of feather.

---

Reading: *1. Tails:*
*2. Japanese Long Tailed Fowl*
Both by Dr Joseph Batty

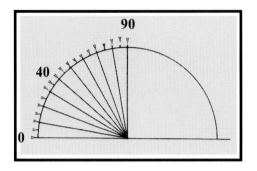

Tail Carriage should be as specified in the Standard and if it departs too far should be penalized.

Generally any tail at 90 degrees or over (Squirrel-tailed) is a serious fault. Japanese bantams are the main exception. But a very low tail will also be serious when the most usual tail angle is specified (eg, $40^0$).

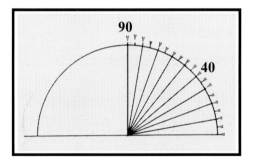

**Tail Angle or Tail Carriage Measure**
Shows the angle as measured in degrees from horizontal.

**Squirrel Tailed**          **Wry Tail (off centre)**

**Split Tail**          **High Tail**

Short
Tail

Fan
Tail

**Faulty Tails**

## FAULTS IN TAILS

The tail is an integral part of the composition of the bird and may make or mar a particular specimen. Usually marks out of 100 are given for the *overall perfect bird* and the tail will represent in the region of 6 to 8 points, although a totally bad tail could cause a bird to lose. This will be for shape/type and colour. It is therefore essential to understand the standard relating to form of the tail, and its angle, as well as the correct colour. The most usual faults are as follows:

**1. Squirrel tail** (90° angle or above) when the angle is required to be normal, ie, in the range 10 to 75 degrees. The most usual range is in the 30 to 45 degree range.

**2. Wry tail** (asymmetrical or lop sided).

**3. Droopy or dropped tail** unless called for in the standard (Malays and other Asian Game).

**4 Split or divided tail.**

**5. Deformities such as a raised or 'roach' back,** which gives the tail an incorrect angle.

**6. Tail at wrong angle.**

**7. Sickle Feathers missing or broken.**

**8. Curved Sickles on a Hen-Cock-type bird; eg, OEG Henny or Sebright.**

**9. Tail on 'Rumpless' fowl.**

**10. Any Other Faults** or defects, including mite on feathers and damaged web of feathers. Possible faults which may be found are:

**(a) Normal feathers on Silkie (instead of being soft and ragged). (b) Angle incorrect because bird does not stand properly; it is essential for birds to be 'pen trained' so the body is at the correct angle which enables the tail to be shown correctly. (c) Wrong colour or a partial wrong colouring such as a bird with a black tail showing white marks. This may be acceptable if there is a strong element of white in the bird; eg, Black Red OEG with white legs and Pile bred, but the standard must be the final word.**

# 7

# LEGS

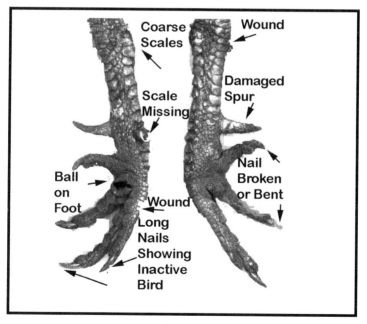

Coarse Scales

Wound

Scale Missing

Damaged Spur

Ball on Foot

Nail Broken or Bent

Wound

Long Nails Showing Inactive Bird

**Faults**

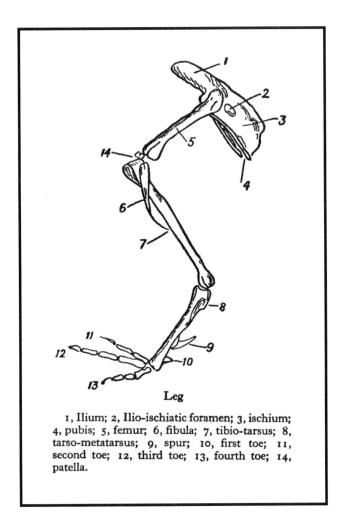

Leg

1, Ilium; 2, Ilio-ischiatic foramen; 3, ischium; 4, pubis; 5, femur; 6, fibula; 7, tibio-tarsus; 8, tarso-metatarsus; 9, spur; 10, first toe; 11, second toe; 12, third toe; 13, fourth toe; 14, patella.

**The Parts of the Leg**
Consists of hip bone, thigh, leg, foot and toes.

# THE LEGS

The legs serve many purposes besides walking and, whilst it is not essential for poultry breeders to know the anatomy terms, it does show the many parts involved. These are indicated on the opposite page and are simply different parts which go to make the whole.

The thigh is the upper part of the leg which joins the hip bone and is usually covered in feathers. The shank or lower leg, including the feet, consists of scales and, with some breeds, feathers appear, growing above the scales.

Usually there are four toes, but on a few breeds there is an extra toe or appendage which appears to serve no purpose.

The legs must be strong enough to stand the weight of the bird and to allow it to scratch and find food. Long nails on a bird are an indication of inactivity and, if on free range or in a run, it is certain that the bird in question is a *waster* and should not be kept.

If kept in an inside training pen for too long the nails will grow because the bird cannot forage and therefore when judging it becomes difficult to know whether to penalize. However, it is a duty for the fancier to ensure that nails are kept short so they should be penalized.

Colour in the shanks is dependant on the breed and may be white, yellow, black, slate, carp, willow or some other specified shade. This may be varied by feeding, by the age of the bird and, a laying hen will tend to lose pigment over a period. The type of land on which the birds are kept also affects the colour, as does the natural food available. Running on grass tends to keep legs very clean and bright, but can be spoilt with mud and other unfavourable conditions.

The colour may be marked in some way with a red line, a pinky shade on white legs, or mottled with a darker colour.

All these differences are specified in the standards and should be present on an exhibition bird. If not, the bird in question should not be eligible for a prize.

## MOVEMENT

A hen or cock has to balance itself on its legs and therefore they must be right or it cannot function. Once a bird "goes of its feet" through injury or disease it quickly deteriorates.

Birds with faulty legs should not be bred from or be shown. At a recent show the author was asked to select Best in Show and a Sebright was put forward as a candidate. When the hen moved, its leg went under the body slightly at the knee so, sadly, although a well marked specimen. it should *not* even have been given a first prize, and could not be considered for a special award.

Birds walk by moving the weight of the body from side to and rotating the knee joints. This places great stress on the legs and any weakness should quickly become apparent, even a slight injury could cause trouble.

The method of walking is also a characteristic of a breed. Some move quickly, others slowly, and the motion should be apparent from study. However, as will be apparent, the slower moving breeds may not exhibit any unfavourable characteristics, but a judge should try to make a bird move around; in addition, when an exhibit is taken from a show pen by the judge the state of the legs should be established to make sure there are no lumps on the thighs or the presence of Scaley Leg or other malady.

## CRITICAL EXAMINATION

When selecting a bird for showing or judging it will be necessary to decide whether the requirements are being covered and, if there are weaknesses, to penalize them by deducting points. In some cases the fault may be serious enough to bar a bird from any prizes despite its other merits. Thus an Old English Game cock which is duck-footed cannot be given a prize, nor can the Dorking without the fourth toe, or the Silkie without feather legs. These are all essential characteristics of the breed and their faults make them fail in terms of the standard.

## Faulty Legs

These apply to all breeds and are a very serious fault.

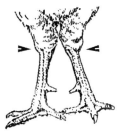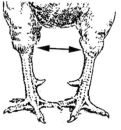

**Knock Knees**          **Bow-Legged**

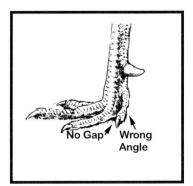

**Duck-footed**
**A Major fault.**

**Web Footed**

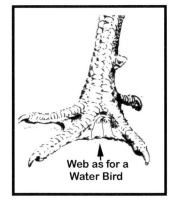

*Drawings after*
*John H Robinson*

Poland
Hen
Lame
with Faults

Lop-Sided
Gait

Small Lump
or Growth

Joint
Swollen

Thick
Instep

Splayed Toes  Long Nail

Corn

Bent Toe

Legs—
incorrect
position.
Too far
forward.

Hen Too Heavy
at Front. Out of
balance. Legs
wrong position.

## Importance of Correct Balance and Symmetry

Each breed has a specific type of carriage, which may be similar. However, there will be subtle variations which can mar a show specimen. The position of the legs and their angle can make a tremendous difference. The reader is referred to page 58 et seq and page 67 in particular where it will be observed that the leg position varies a good deal.

Legs on
Modern Game
Long & Elegant.
Often Stand on
Toes & Cause
Back Toe to
Be Off Floor
Level.

Acceptable
in Moderns,
but not OEG.

Back Toe
Well off
Ground

Floor
Level

## COLOUR OF LEGS

The colour of the leg is critical in all varieties of **Modern Game** and no deviation should be permitted. This is not necessarily the case with Old English Game where some latitude is permitted, although strictly the colour of the variety and the legs should match; it would be wrong to have a light coloured bird with, say, black legs.

Moderns' leg colours are:

| _Black_ | _Yellow_ | _Willow_ | _Blue_ |
|---------|----------|----------|--------|
| Birchen | Pile (Pyle) * | Duckwings | Blue |
| Brown Red | White | Black Reds | Lemon Blue |
| Black | | | |

*Pyle is the USA spelling, although recently introduced into the British standard.

## Light Sussex Faults in Legs, Carriage and Tail

Sussex should have white legs and feet for all varieties. This has an important bearing on its table properties for it is an excellent table fowl—white skin and flesh.

Birds with yellow legs have yellow skin and these are not generally appreciated in England, although in recent times a 'Corn-fed Capone' has been marketed, whch has yellow legs and skin.

Some utility birds such as the Plymouth Rock and Rhode Island Red also have yellow legs.

Light breeds which have yellow legs are Leghorns, but in the case of the Black variety there are difficulties because yellow and black are unnatural companions and double mating may have to be practised.

All interact on each other so when legs are wrong other aspects affected.,

## Indian Game with Faulty Feet & Toes

**There is a tendency for heavy birds to have rather poor feet and legs which
are coarse. Shanks should be round and flat shins are a fault.
On the other hand, when dealing with a closely related breed, the Aseel
(Asil) the legs would be expected to be squarish,
a characteristic of the breed and not round shanked like OEG.**

## COLOUR OF LEGS

Indian Game and related hard feathered breeds have yellow
legs. Thus there are Aseel, Malays, Shamos and Indian Game which
have yellow legs, the deeper the better. Usually they have a red line
down the side. The deep yellow may get paler with the age of the
bird.

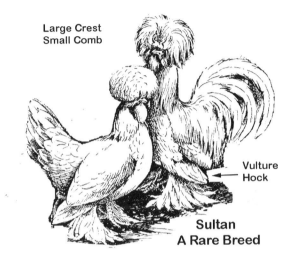

Large Crest
Small Comb

Vulture
Hock

Sultan
A Rare Breed

Full Feathered legs and vulture hocks which are not allowed on most other large breeds. Some do have vulture hocks; eg, Booted Bantams and Breda fowl. However, other feathered leg breeds should not have vulture hocks and in the USA is penalised for such breeds as Brahmas and Cochins.

## Pekin Bantam
Must have profuse feathering on legs. Globular in shape. Booting sticking out at side is a serious fault. Head should 'tilt' slightly.

See *Pekin Bantams* Margaret Gregson

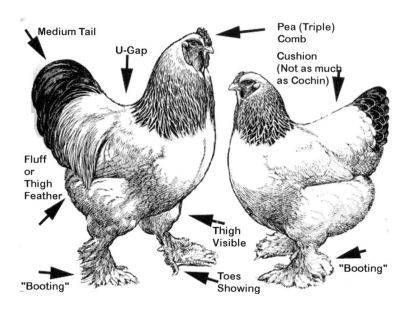

Medium Tail
U-Gap
Pea (Triple) Comb
Cushion (Not as much as Cochin)
Fluff or Thigh Feather
Thigh Visible
Toes Showing
"Booting"
"Booting"

## Light Brahmas

These are Asiatic like the Cochins and have a number of features in common such as massive size with mature cocks being around 12lb for Brahma and 13lb (5.90k) for Cochins. They have yellow legs and face bright red.
Differences are in the comb and feathering with the Cochin being more profusely feathered. More leg shows on the Brahma the thighs being visible.
In both the shank feathering should be plentiful, but serious faults are broken or dirty feathers, and vulture hocks.

## White Cochins    (OPPOSITE)

 The bantams of this breed are known by the same name in the USA, but regarded as a separate breed in Britain under the name of Pekins, which tend to be relatively lower and rounder. See Notes on Brahma.
NOTES
1. The gap between the Fluff (bottom) and the Booting (top) should be minimal, preferably not at all. See *Pekin* preceding page.
2. The tail of the cock above is on the high side, but emphasized   because he is bending over to offer the worm.

**White Cochins ( Notes Opposite)**

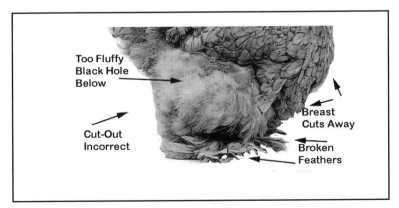

**Cochin With Serious Faults**

This cut out of bottom part of hen shows faulty circle in body, thus not complying with correct shape. Feathers broken on shanks and feet. The body shape should be round.

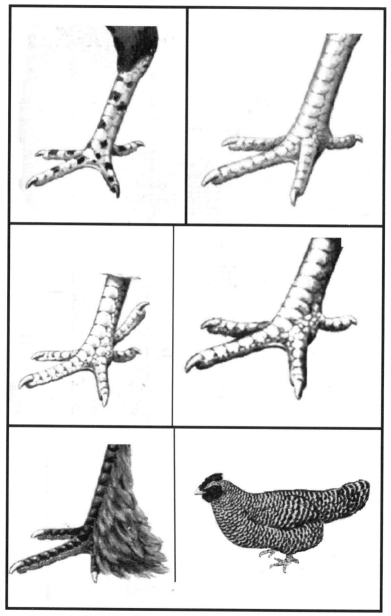

**Legs and Feet for Different Breeds.**

|  |  |
|---|---|
| **Mottled Legs**<br>Ancona Yellow<br>with even<br>black mottles.<br>Scots Grey<br>White with<br>black mottles | **Flat Sided**<br>No Feathers<br>eg, Aseel |
| **Five-toed**<br>(Polydactyly)<br>Dorkings<br>Silkies<br>Faverolle<br>Houdan | **Rounded Shanks**<br>Most breeds,<br>but Game OEG &<br>Modern critical |
| **Moderate Feathering**<br>on Shanks and outer<br>Toe only.<br>eg, Croad Langshan,<br>Modern Langshan<br>North Holland Blue | **Very Short**<br>Legs<br>Scots Dumpy<br>German Bantam<br>Dutch Creeper<br>Courtes-Pattes<br><br>Many breeding<br>problems; lethal<br>genes. |

Cushion
Comb
Purple

Tail should be very soft.
This is too hard feathered.

Feathering
on
Shank
& Middle
Toe

Middle Toe
Feathering

**Essentials of the Silkie Cock.**
Note the five toes. A bantam and large size exist, but in USA bantam only.
Middle toe without feathers is serious defect.

## LEG COLOUR

Leg colour can be quite confusing so the reader is advised to study the standard for the breed in question. They may be white, black, slate, and yellow. Sometimes there are optional choices, but usually a main colour prevails for a variety.

# 8

# OTHER
# FEATURES

*The Standards lay down many special features for breeds and often these "show points" become quite exaggerated as a result of breeders striving for perfection. As shown in Chapter 3 under Key factors a small number of features can amount to as much as 50 or more points.*

*These special features must be understood by the fancier and the knowledge applied. It is also useful to have a basic understanding of the genetics involved in the improvement of the feature.*

SPIKES

CREST

COMB

COMB

WHISKERS

BEARD

NOSTRIL

EYE

EAR

BEAK

EAR LOBE

WATTLES

NECK HACKLE

SICKLES

BACK

SADDLE

TAIL

SHOULDER COVERTS

WING BOW

BREAST

WING COVERT OR "BAR

WING BAY

THIGH

TAIL COVERTS OR SIDE HANGERS

SADDLE HACKLE

SECONDARIES WHICH COVER THE PRIMARIES OR FLIGHTS

LEG OR SHANK

SPUR

TOES

BACK TOE- SHOULD TOUCH FLOOR

## Main Features of the Fowl
**Reference should also be made to earlier chapters on Combs, Legs, Tails, etc.**

# OTHER REQUIREMENTS

The fowl has many features and, although some are similar, very rarely will a breed be the same as another. In fact, even within a breed the different varieties may have significant differences in size and other characteristics. Variations in combs, legs, tail, feathering and so on are quite common. Study of the standards is essential to see what these are; for example, look at the Araucana which may have a tail or be rumpless. or the Orpington and Dorking which have different varieties which are not the same size; when dealing with Old English Game there are tassels, crests and even a variety where the cock has "hen feathering".

The most important terms are:

**1. Back** which included the shoulders and saddle, forming the area across the top of the body.

**2. Barring** which is the term used to describe the alternate bars on the body. This is really a self colour to which a barring factor is added in the genetic make-up.It is similar to 'Cuckoo' but usually barring is more exact. The term is also used in connection with Pencilling with the Hamburg.

**3. Beard** which is the formation of feathers found on certain breeds which, combined with muffs, becomes 'Muffles'.

**4. Crescent** which is the shape of the moon and therefore describes a marking of this shape.

**5. Crest** —a rounded formation of feathers which appear on the head of a fowl. A split, or lopsided, or asymmetric crest is a defect.

**6. Cuckoo** marking which is a form of indefinite barring.

**7. Cushion** which is the mound of feathers on the saddle, notably on the Cochin.

8. Defect which is a feature not in accordance with the standard.

9. Dewlap which is a loose pouch under the beak or bill seen on the Brahma and the Toulouse Goose.

10. Dubbing (Dubbed) which is the practice of removing the comb of a male bird to comply with show requirements in OEG amd Modern Game. It is also done to avoid damage or frost bite.

11. Duckfooted when the back toe is at the side.

12. Ears which are small apertures at the side of the head, but the deaf ear or face lobe, which serves no useful purpose, is often white and of a large size.

13. Ear Lobe which is a round or elongated section of skin which is below the ear proper and may be white, red, purple or blue.

14. Edging on feathers which may be a different colour as in lacing or a lighter or darker shade of the same colour. This is seen on Orpingtons in the same colour, eg, blue, or in Columbian birds where the edging is white and there is a blue or black centre.

15. Enamel White which is used to describe the kid-like texture and colour on the lobes of Rosecombs and Mediterranean breeds of poultry. A black, blue, red or other colour on the white is serious.

16. Flat Shin or Shank which is a fault on a breed requiring rounded shanks.

17. Frosting which is a shading on the web of a feather which is supposed to be a specific colour. An example is the Sebright bantam when black or other dark colour appears on the gold or silver.

18. Hard Feathered which described the feathering of Game breeds and varieties, each feather being lacking in fluff and is tightly wrapped around the body. The opposite is soft feathered, but many breeds are in between and therefore there should be a medium classification.

19. Lacing which consists of a narrow band of a different colour around a feather, usually fairly narrow. Usually single, but can be double in Barnevelder hens and cocks or on Indian Game hens.
*Cont. page 120*

## Barring

The best known of the Barred breeds is the Barred Plymouth Rock. This consists of alternate light and dark colours — Blueish white and almost black. These marks must be quite positive and clear not mingling with the lighter areas as in the Cuckoo breeds such as the Marans. The bars are also relatively straight whereas in Cuckoo breeds the bars are more crescentic.

Some breeds, which are referred to as being Barred, are more of the Cuckoo type. This applies to Scots Greys which has equal barring, but certainly not as exact as Barred Plymouth Rocks.

### Ideal Barring on Plymouth Rocks

**There should be no other colours and the barring should be positive and even.**

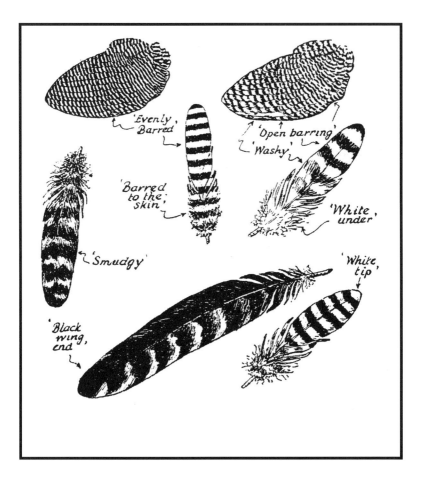

**Faults in Barring**
**Top Left Correct; balance have faults as indicated.**

Mediterranean TYPE Combs

Silver Hackle

Hen Feathering

Bars (Green Black) 3 times width of silver ground colour.

## Silver Campines

These present an interesting phenomenon because the bars are three times as wide as the ground colour, which should be white in the Silver Campine and Gold in the Gold variety. The bars should be black with a greenish sheen. The hackle should be silver or gold to match the ground colour.

It should be noted that this breed is *hen feathered* meaning that the tail of the cock should not be curved with sickles.

The genetic composition of the Campine is not the same as the Barred Plymouth Rock

## Brakel (Braekel)

This related breed is similar to the Campine except the back, including the saddle and hackles are silver or deep gold (golden bay); in other words, the bars do not extend over the body, but stop short just above the wings. The bars are *twice the width* instead or three times as in the Campine.

This affects the input of colour and the result is the tail is virtually black although, according to the British standard, there should be markings on the tail. It is not hen feathered.

The British standard appears to be incorrect because the hen portrayed by Sir Edward Brown *(Poultry Breeding & Production)* does not have solid colour on the back, but the male does.

## CUCKOO MARKINGS

The precise barring of the Plymouth Rock is due to a gene which limits the colour and produces the lighter ground colour. However, this is not the full story—behind the achievement of the breeding is the careful selection of birds over many generations. This very special barring means that the breed tends to develop slower than the breeds with less precise markings.

Where the bars are less precisely marked the term "Cuckoo" is used. The standards call this *irregular banding*. Examples of breeds incolved are:

**Leghorn (Cuckoo)**

**Maline**

**Marans**

**North Holland Blues**

**Orpington (May be cuckoo or barred)**

**Scots Greys**

The Cuckoo Leghorn standard specifies that the bands should be distinct (not running into the other colour), but not as distinct as barring (eg, Plymouth Rock style).

The others follow a similar pattern. The Marans may be Dark, Gold or Silver, the darker and lighter colours submerging into each other, although still distinct. Exact barring should *not* be the aim if this leads to loss of utility.

North Holland Blues are regarded as a "barred" breed, but, in reality, are Cuckoo. Like the Marans they must be treated as a utility breed. The Orpington with cuckoo markings is now returning in Germany and may be revived in other countries.

Scots Greys are also viewed as "barred" and this aspect has improved, but there is still a tendency towards being cuckoo. The black bars are not as perfect as Plymouth Rocks and vary in different parts of the body.

**Original Type of Scots Grey showing the Cuckoo Markings**

**Detail of Cuckoo Bands
for Scots Grey hen (above).**

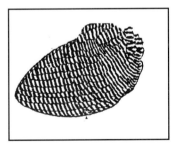

**Detail from Plymouth Rock
Note the evenness of the barring.**

TERMS (Cont.)

20.Muffling which consists of the beard and whiskers of certain breeds. Seen in Houdans and Faverolles.

21. Pencilling (Pencilled) when there are lines, stripes or fine marks on various breeds such as Pencilled Hamburghs (fine lines) or Partridge breeds such as Cochins, Old English Game and Wyandottes.

22. Peppering which are small marks, sometimes in clusters, which are a defect on a specific colour.

23. Smut (Smutty) which is dark undercolour instead of the natural colour such as red in Rhode Island Reds.

24. Spangling (Spangled) which consists of white spots or marks, sometimes accompanied by a black line as in Speckled Sussex, but also refers to OEG, and in a separate category, Anconas which are really V-shaped marks. Also under this category are the *Mottles* found on certain breeds like the Houdan. (See *Tipped* below)

25. Spurred which is required on a male bird and is regarded with favour on a Game female. The Sumatra may have a double spur. Absence of spurs on an adult male should be regarded as a defect.

26. Stub which is the base of a feather on a featherless legged birds and is therefore a fault. In the USA regarded as a disqualification.

27. Tipped which means having white marks on the darker feathers such as in Anconas which have V-marks. (See *Spangles* above)

28. Twisted Feathers, usually in the hackle, but could be found any where. OEG suffer from dry hackle which causes problems.

29. Under-Colour which is the part of the feather which is not visible.

30.Wing Parts which consist of BAR, BAY, BOW, BUTTS and which are a vital part of the show requirements. (See page 112)

## BEARDS & OTHER ADDITIONS

One of the great attractions of poultry is the fact that there is so much variety. Beards, Crests, Tassels and Muffs are some of the different features which may be found, all of which must comply with the standards. The French breeds are especially inclined towards these additions.

### Houdan  (Mottled Houdan)

**This breed has many unusual features. The crest should be rounded and full without any splits. The Muffling should be full and consist of Beard and Side Whiskers (Muffs). Many modern specimens do not reach the high standard portrayed above the crest being small and muffling weak.**

**The marks on the green-black plumage are white and should be fairly even in size; they are a form of spangle but referred to as 'Mottles'. The latter differ from Spangles proper because they appear on parts of the plumage, not necessarily even and regular.**

**Anconas have V-shaped mottles or marks.**

### Old English Game Showing Muffs and Tassels

The 'Muffs' which have been highlighted are a form of beard. The Tassels appear at the back of the head like a badly formed crest.

Other breeds do have muffs, beards and tassels, but not exactly like these. Thus the Appenzeller has a crest or tassel which stands erect and leans forward; the Araucana also has a crest as does the Watermael bantam. Breda (weak tassel), Silkies, Sumtala (tassel)

The Faverolles has muffs and beard and the Sultan has muffles and crest.

*The fancier and judge must be able to distinguish the different types and forms.*

# LACING

One of the difficult areas is the question of lacing which often means different things for different breeds. In the main it is a border of distinct colour around the edge of a feather; thus we have distinct lacing on Polands and Sebright bantams. This marking must be even, of the correct width, and of the correct colour and shade.

When judging it is advisable to place fingers under the feathers, when it should be apparent that the lacing is correct, without any frosting or mismarking on the web. Simply glancing at the ends of feathers is not good enough, because faults may not be detected.

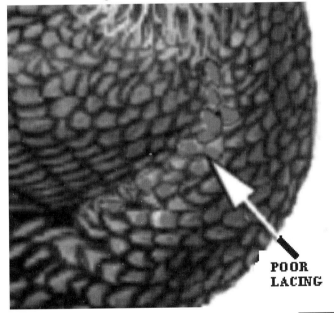

POOR
LACING

**Gold Laced Wyandotte**
**Detail from bird opposite.**
**Smudges and frosting are common faults**
**See *The Sebright Bantam* for a detailed coverage.**
**Other faults are lacing missing, part double lacing,**
**V-shaped Lacing, and irregular lines.**

Some breeds have 'double lacing' which means that there must be a distinct double row on the feathers. The two main breeds are Indian Game (females) and Barnevelders, full in the female and partial in the male. This characteristic is of vital importance and without the correct form cannot hope to win at shows.

**Barnevelder
Hen showing
Double lacing
on tail, breast
and shoulders.**

*Below*
**Detail from
Hen above.**

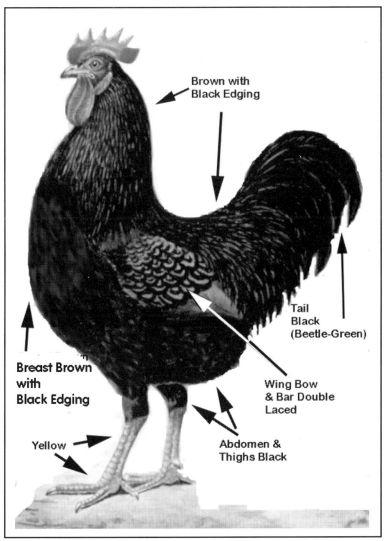

Brown with
Black Edging

Tail
Black
(Beetle-Green)

Breast Brown
with
Black Edging

Wing Bow
& Bar Double
Laced

Yellow

Abdomen &
Thighs Black

## Barnevelder Cock

Although 'Double Laced' for both female and male this is not as prominent in
the latter the term 'Edging' being more appropriate. In the British Standards
the photographs show the male overwhelmed by the Beetle-green Black and
the edging not distinct.

## Faults in Lacing on Single Lacing

"Double Laced" —black lacing should be round edge of feather so this is a fault. Not be confused with proper *Double Lacing* on Barnevelders and Indian Game.

Spangled Feather— not lacing.

Almond Feather—Too narrow for Wyandottes, but correct for Sebrights.

Open Feather—broader and more correct for Wyandotte, but not Sebright.

Mossy Feather—destroys the lacing; bad fault.

Ticked Feathers— not usually regarded as very serious, but clean feather preferred.

Irregular Lacing— spoils lacing; common on breasts of cocks; serious.

Streaky Feathers— again a serious fault, spoils lacing completely.

**Silver Sebright**
**Narrow Feathers**
**Perfect Lacing**

**See Possible**
**Faults Opposite**

**Silver Poland(s) or Polish**
*Stds* state:
 Lacing (USA);
**Lacing or**
**Spangled (British)**
The tendency is
to Laced.

This breed does
not attract a lot
of attention because
in the large the quality
has deteriorated.
Bantams are popular,
but crests need to be
improved.
Crest in hen is Globular.
Lacing best after first
full moult.

Full Crest
Even
No Splits

Tail Full
Laced

Globular
Laced

No Comb
Preferred

Full
Lacing

## Lacing to Mean Pencilling

The so-called Pencilling on the Pencilled Wyandotte is in reality a form of lacing, but in triple form.

The pencilling should consist of three or more pencil marks extending into the feathers.

### Silver Pencilled Wyandotte
(Pencilling the same for *Partridge* variety—difference in colour.)

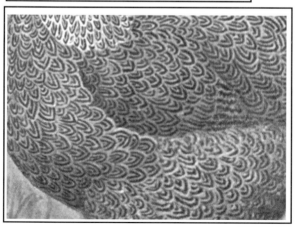

**Detail for above Hen.**

## Further Pencilling

A breed which causes some difficulty is the Hamburgh because different terms are used. It should be noted the Pencilled means *Barring* when applied to Silver and Gold Pencilled Hamburghs.

For exhibition purposes it was usual to double mate, but after about 1949 Harry Snowden a well known breeder managed to produce Silver Spangled from one pen. These increased numbers being shown, but they are still not a popular breed.

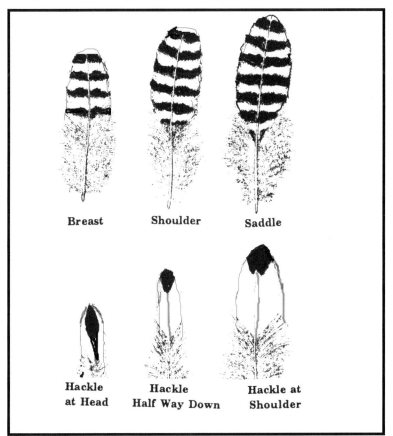

Breast          Shoulder          Saddle

Hackle          Hackle          Hackle at
at Head     Half Way Down      Shoulder

**Guide to Pencilling (Barrring) [Top] and Spangles [Bottom]**
**Fine pencilling is desired and spangles rounded.**

Redcaps
Hen Half
Moon Spangles

Golden Spangled
Hamburghs

Silver Spangled Hamburgh

Silver Pencilled
Hamburgh

Mooney Cock
Spangled
Hamburghs
came from
Mooneys

S. Pencilled
Henny Cock

Black Hamburghs.
Old Type

Gold Spangled
Hamburghs
Spangling Even

Black Hamburghs

(After Ludlow)

## Hamburghs & Redcaps
**These came from the same base stock of Mooneys and
Yorkshire Pheasant Fowl**

## Spangling as in Old English Game

Probably the most popular of bantams, the Spangle Old English Game is one of the most attractive. Rare in large Game, although kept by the author for many years, the bantam variety always turns out in large numbers. As a result competition is very keen and only top birds will win.

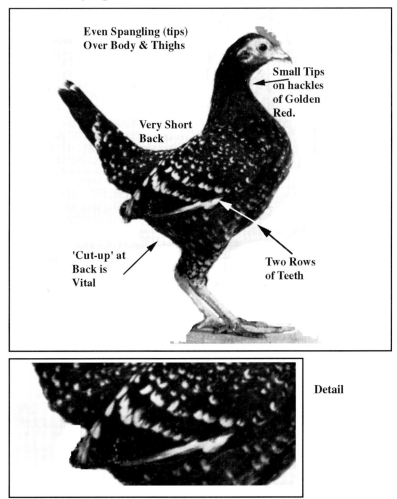

Even Spangling (tips) Over Body & Thighs

Small Tips on hackles of Golden Red.

Very Short Back

'Cut-up' at Back is Vital

Two Rows of Teeth

Detail

Tail Black
Preferably
Tipped

Dark
Red with
Small Tips

Black
Breast
Even
Tips

Bar
Metallic
Blue

Overall
Dark
Burgundy

## Old English Game Spangle Bantam Cockerel

Level spread of spangles is desired against a background of Dark Partridge for the hen and Burgundy and Black for the Male bird.

Large Game are in a different category having much more white and the colours tending to be lighter overall. In some strains the tail is quite white, simply because it is a light red OEG with spangles imposed.

# TIP-TYPE SPANGLES
# AND SPLASHES

There are markings which appear on birds and are loosely termed *spangles,* but are not strictly true spangles. These consist of 'Tips' which appear on Anconas and Spangled Sussex, and 'Splashes' which are found on a variety of breeds where Blues are being bred. Houdans also have mottles which should be even and clear. The exhibitor or judge must realize which of these categories he is dealing with.

Splashed birds cause confusion simply because they are fairly uncommon and unless an exhibitor is accustomed to them, he may believe that they must be even and regular, which is not always the case.

NEATLY DUBBED
COMB (ESSENTIAL
FOR OEG)

NARROW
AT TAIL

BREAST
BROAD

SPLASHES ARE
IRREGULAR, BUT
FORM A REASONABLY
NEAT PATTERN

## The Wings

The wings are an integral part of each breed of poultry and the standards specify their position, colour and markings. Often the markings on the wings are an indication on whether the correct balance of colour is present; thus, in the Rhode Island Red the lower web should be black, to an exact measure, and if the black runs over the main colour will be too dark.

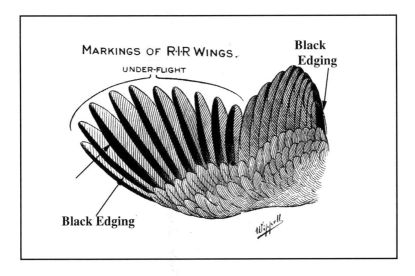

The wings when open should be red and black—the primary flights have the outside webbing black, and in the secondaries the reverse. If the wing is spread out the outside webbing of the first ten flights should be black, and the inside red. With the remaining ten feathers, nearest the body, the webbing nearest the body should be black and the other side red.

# 9

# LIKELY DEFECTS

*Defects may be classified in a variety of ways and must be penalized at shows. Different views exist on how they should be dealt with. For example, in the Ancona standard reductions such as in-kneed 10 points, crooked toes 10 points, bad comb 5 points, and white in face 20 points (a massive reduction). In the USA there is a General Scale of Points which allows birds to be judged on the basis of all the main features such as symmetry (4), weight (4), condition (10), comb (5), etc.*

*Birds with serious faults may be disqualified usually on the grounds of <u>failing on breed characteristics</u>, or <u>having a disease or serious condition</u>, or <u>faking</u> such as dyeing or cutting away parts or replacing feathers. Simple defects are not serious enough for disqualification and the Disqualification Penalty should be used with discretion.*

*If birds are placed in the wrong class they may be "Passed" which is fairer than a disqualification.*

## <u>RECOGNISED FACTORS WHICH MAY BE USED</u>
## <u>TO "PASS" OR DISQUALIFY</u>

In grooming likely winners the fancier must recognise birds with potential, but also those which have serious faults, which might cause them to be downgraded or to be disqualified. Such features should not be tolerated because it is likely that any stock *bred* from the birds which offend will also be faulty, hence the strictness called for in judging.

# Examples:

## In all Birds — GENERAL DEFECTS

*Structural deformities or alien characteristics:*
**Roach back, deformed comb, twisted beak, wrongly angled legs, blindness, wry or squirrel tail, wrong colour legs, wrong number of toes, wrong colour feet, feathered legs on clean legged breeds, wrong colour eyes, twisted toes, duck-footed, flat shanks (Modern and OEG), bad carriage, split or slipped wing, excessively fat, vulture hocks (except Sultans and Booted) bumble foot, wrong colour plumage, or any other serious defect.** *Signs of Faking —very serious.*

|  | *DEFECTS* |
|---|---|
| **Ancona:** | **White faced, red in earlobes, soft featherings; incorrect tipping, wrong comb, wrong colour legs, defective tails.** |
| **Andalusian, Leghorns, Minorcas:** | **Not complying with Mediterranean type. Poor comb, red on ear lobes, etc.** |
| **Aseel:** | **Roach back, soft feathered, round shanks, not pugnacious, lacking beetle brow, tail above horizontal, legs not bent at hocks.** |
| **Australorp** | **Lacking Utility aspects, foul feathering, white in ear lobes, excess feathering, long back. yellow eyes, feathered legs.** |

----- *The reader is advised to memorize the general faults because they may apply to very many breeds.*

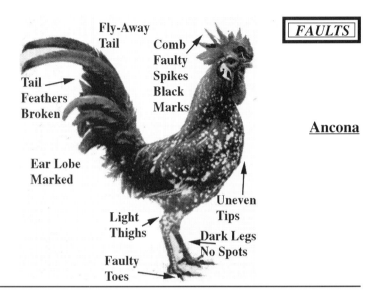

Fly-Away Tail

Comb Faulty Spikes Black Marks

Tail Feathers Broken

**FAULTS**

**Ancona**

Ear Lobe Marked

Light Thighs

Uneven Tips

Dark Legs No Spots

Faulty Toes

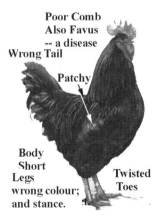

Poor Comb Also Favus -- a disease

Wrong Tail

Patchy

Body Short Legs wrong colour; and stance.

Twisted Toes

## Australorp
**Many faults, including uneven comb
and those shown above**

| Breed | Defects |
|---|---|
| **Barnevelder\*** | Double Laced: Wrong colour legs, wrong shape, lacking double lacing, wrong colour, white in lobes, and any other uncharacteristic feature. |
| **Belgian Bantams**<br>Barbu d'Anvers<br>Barbu d'Uccle<br>Barbu d'Watermael | Strong wattles, wrong type comb, absence of beard/whiskers, feather legs (d'Anvers) or lack of feathers ( d'Uccle), more than 4 toes, too large, wrong type of tail. Lacking "Type"—shape, carriage, etc. |
| **Brahma:** | No leg feathers, vulture hocks, lack of size, poor pencilling where required, lacking balance, too feathery. |
| **Bresse:** | Coarseness, lack of depth, loose feathering, wrong type of comb, lacking laying characteristics. |
| **Campine:** | Curved sickles on cocks, bars incorrect width, ground colour not clear, comb following neck, white face, white toe nails, beak dark, featherlegs, hackle incorrect shade, dark around eyes. |
| **Cochin:** | No leg feathers, foul feathering eg, dark spots on Buffs, brown mottling on Partridge, too small, lacking copious feathering and cushion. |
| **Croad Langshan:** | Yellow legs, yellow on face, white in ear lobes, black on soles, foul feathering, vulture hocks, incorrect leg feathering. |
| **Dorking:** | No fourth toe, dark legs, wrong comb for variety, tallness, lack of size, shallow keel, foul feathering for variety. |

**\*For all breeds see *General Defects* on page 136.**

**Brahmas**

Poor Combs

**Dark Brahmas**

Tail White Feathers

Hackle No Black Stripes

Small Bodied

Pencilling Indistinct

Mottling on Black

Vulture Hocks

Vulture Hocks

Sparse Feathering

Comb Too Large & Beefy.

FAULTS

Sickle Missing

Back Too Short

Tail Too High

Baggy Featherimg

Twisted Toes

**Bresse Cock**

| | |
|---|---|
| **Dutch Bantam:** | Incorrect colour, whip tail, large ear lobes, white in face, foul feathering, lacking low wings, long back, shallow breast, long legs, narrow shoulders, and rounded back. |
| **Faverolles:** | Four toes only, no muffling, legs not feathered. |
| **Frizzle:** | Lacking curl in feathers. |
| **Hamburgh:** | In Spangled - the spangles too large, often running into each other.<br>In Pencilled —bars are irregular and patchy. |
| **Houdan:** | Lacking five toes, feathered legs, colours other than green-black with white mottles. |
| **Indian Game:** | Narrowness, too tall, not properly laced, single comb, light colour in legs. |
| **Japanese Bantams:** | High standing, narrow body, short tail, non-standard comb or lobes, high wings. |
| **Jersey Giant:** | Smallness in size, too feathery. |
| **Leghorn:** | Coarseness, faulty comb, red earlobes, white legs, squirrel tail in male or fan tail in female, light coloured legs. |
| **Malay:** | Lacking size, loose or fluffy feather, upright tail, small head.<br><br>Compare Shamo which is similar in carriage. |
| *For all breeds see *General Defects* on page 136.* | |

**Duckwing Frizzle with Faults**

Neck Feathers Lying Flat

Tail Raggy

Legs Rough (Scaley Leg ?)

Wings Flat Lack of Curl Overall.

Under-developed Comb

Head Narrow Lacking 'Beetle Brow'.

JUBILEE INDIAN GAME COCK

Thin, Weak Neck.

Narrow Overall. Lacking Bone. Breast Narrow.

Legs Rough Lacking Pigment

Twisted Toes

| | |
|---|---|
| **Marans:** | Not utility type, feathers on legs, lacking cuckoo pattern in colours. |
| **Minorca:** | Small ear lobes, blemishes on ear lobes, tail wrong angle, heavy body, short back. |
| **Modern Game:** | Coarseness, feathery, short legs, lacking reach, rounded back, long back, lack of style, wrong colours in plumage, legs or eyes, duck-footed, not dubbed in male birds. |
| **Modern Langshan:** | Short legs, feathering on shanks incorrect, not 'hard' and glossy, lack of 'reach', wrong colour legs/feet, coarseness, wrong colours in plumage. |
| **Nankin (Bantam):** (*Nankin* means a Buff colour.) | White on ear lobes, long legs, colour defects, lacking jaunty character, lacking full breast, no black end to female tail, wrong colour legs. |
| **New Hampshire Red:** | Loose feathering, wrong colours, lacking full breast, wings low, smutty under colour, lack of black on tail, light coloured legs, white on face, no black edging on coverts, pale eyes. |
| **Norfolk Grey:** | Feathering on legs, too soft feathered, wrong coloured plumage, eg, brassy or mossy; light coloured legs, narrowness. |
| **North Holland Blue:** | Lacking shank feathers, coarseness, non-utility features, long back, shallow breast. |
| **Old English Game:** | Lacking flat back, narrow shoulders, v.short legs, drooping wings, too fat, wrong colour in colour classes, coarseness. undubbed cock, beetle browed, light eyed, duck footed, bantam (English) stunted or long tail, mopey. |
| *For all breeds see General Defects on page 136.* | |

| | |
|---|---|
| **Old English Pheasant Fowl:** | Red in lobes, poor comb, incorrect markings on breast, body and tail, fineness of body, weak tail, small body. |
| **Orloff:** | No muffling, wrong type comb, lacking upright carriage, high tail, v. short back. |
| **Orpington:** | Lacking utility, wrong colour, smallness, fluffy in feathers, legs hidden, yellow skin or shanks, long legs, white ear lobes, excess abdomen feathers, plumage showing purple, too much cushion. |
| **Pekin Bantams:** | Wrong colour legs, faulty colouring, legs showing, eyes wrong colour, faulty carriage, high tail, lack of feathers. |
| **Plymouth Rock:** | Poor colouring (including barring), feathering on legs, duckfooted, thin thighs, lacking size, cut away front, lack of utility features. |
| **Poland:** | Faulty crest, poor lacing (on laced types), fluffy, incorrect comb, short hackle, stork legged, feather duster appearance, squirrel tail, wrong carriage, mopey. |
| **Redcap:** | Weak head points —comb too small, coarse, narrow, twisted leader, etc. ; low or too high tail; wrong colour in plumage, white ear lobes, feather on legs. At one time combs were about 5ins (12.5cm) wide, but 3ins (7.5cm) is more likely. |
| **Rhode Island Red:** | Wrong colour or incorrect black markings, high tail, feathers on shanks, white ear lobes, short back, lacking breadth, coarseness, weak breast, under weight, wrong under colour. |
| *For all breeds see *General Defects* on page 136.* | |

**Weak Head & Face. Lack of Utility.**

**Abdomen Too Feathery**

**Legs Not Visible** →

**Toes Twisted** ⟵

**Black Orpington Hen: Excessive Feathering.**

**Chamois Poland**

**Lacing Variable & Patchy.**

**Tail Set Rather Low. Stds call for tail set low, but not as horizontal as shown.**

**Patchy in Feathers.**

**Detailed Faults— Rhode Island Reds**
From *The RIR Fowl,* J Batty.

| | |
|---|---|
| **Rosecomb Bantams:** | Faulty head points (comb and ear lobes), short tail, narrow sickles, sickles too long, shallow breast, long back, narrow at shoulders, low wings, stilty legs, faulty colours. |
| **Scots Dumpies:** | Tallness, short body, wrong carriage, ear lobes  white, faulty plumage. |
| **Scots Greys:** | Soft feathered, barring faulty, colours other than steel grey with black bars, dumpy, dark legs, weak breast, low tail, lacking vigour, eyes wrong colour. |
| **Sebright Bantams:** | Large and cloddy, poor lacing, frosting or other  marks, sickle feathers in male, loose feathering, wrong shade, long back, faulty comb, white ear lobes, wide feathers (almond shape required). |
| **Shamo:**<br><br>Note: The Shamo bantam is a more cobby bird, not as upright as the large fowl. | Horizontal carriage, tail above horizontal, red eyes, too feathery, wrong shape, light col-oured legs, long hackle feathers, small in stature. wattles, wrong comb, thin thighs. |
| **Sicilian Buttercup and Sicilian Firebird:** | Imperfect comb, wrong colours, over-size, low tail, no sickle feathers, profuse feathering. |
| **Silkies:** | Hard feathering, sickle feathers, wrong, shape, only four toes, no feathering on legs, comb other than cushion type, vulture hocks, lack of crest or beard (when appropriate), bright red face, green on beak, soles of  feet green tinge, wrong colouring, scaly leg. |

*For all breeds see *General Defects* on page 136.

Sickle Feathers

White Ear Lobe

Poor Lacing on Tail

Overall Lacing Poor

Carriage Incorrect

Wings Should be Pointing Down

Dark & Light Patches

**Golden Sebright Male with Faults**

Weak Tail

Lacking Broad Body

Breast Weak

**SCOTS GREY COCKEREL**

| | |
|---|---|
| **Spanish:** | Faults on face piece including colour blemishes, coarseness, short in stature, feathery, excessive face 'decoration', plumage colour incorrect, tail at wrong angle. |
| **Sultan:** | Ornamental features in correct: comb, crest (split or lop sided), legs not fully feathered, no vulture hocks, only four toes, wings carried high, tail small or at wrong angle. |
| **Sumatra (Game):** | Soft feathered, short back, upright in car riage, single comb, short tail, asymmetrical in shape, lacking green sheen on deep, glossy black, light red face. |
| **Sussex:** | Wrong colour for variety, lacking size, short back, cushion, legs and skin other than white, rose combs, not according to utility type, excess feathering. |
| **Transylvanian Naked Neck:** | Feathers on neck, scales on neck, fluffy plumage, short legs, tail at incorrect angle. |
| **Tuzo Bantam:** | See Shamo. |
| **Vorwerk:** | Wrong colour mixture, lack of depth in body, narrow body, high tail, coarseness, red in lobes, excessive feathering. |
| **Welsummer:** | Feathering on legs, stripes in hackle (male), purely black breast (male), light colour breast in female, legs not yellow, lacking utility. |
| **Wyandotte:** | Plumage colour defects for variety, comb other than cradle type, lacking roundness for breed, faulty lacing in the laced varieties, legs wrong colour, too feathery, legs not visible. |
| **Yokohama: Phoenix** | Stunted feathers in saddle or tail feathers, blemishes on face, single comb, tail above horizontal, goose winged, lacking |

*For all breeds see *General Defects* on page 136.

Comb Lacking Width

Tail:
Lacking Sickles
Broken/Stunted
Incorrect Angle

Back Rather Long

Breast Not Full Enough

REDCAP
COCKEREL

Comb Faulty
Does not follow
neck (inverted cradle)

Broken Tail

Back Incorrect

Body not rounded enough.

Shallow Breast

White
 Wyandotte
 Cock

# TRIOS

At major show it may be possible to show two hens and a matching cock. Although a fancier has to go to a great deal of trouble with a trio a well matched presentation does much to recommend the breeder in question. The birds should comply with the standard and be the appropriate size and on an even basis. The ASP (USA standards) suggest rules for judging Trios and these stipulate that, *when there is a tie,* the one which contains the best male should win. In judging, the male is worth 50 per cent of the marks and the two females the other half and these should be a matching pair in terms of size, colour and other points.

**Training Pen with Exhibitor Using Judging Stick**
See Text in Chapter 10 for technique.

# 10

# SHOW
# PREPARATION

Lacing Not Positive Enough

Tail Weak

Too small.
Lacks rounded
shape.

Long, thin
Legs

**Barred Plymouth Rock Hen**
Not typical of  breed so should not be bred from.

Section of Training Pens in Penning Room or Shed.

These are made of wood with wire fronts and a number of rows can be arranged. Keep the water containers clean and replenish daily.

Handle the birds regularly to train for shows and also use a judging stick.
*Bottom:* Training Pens made of wire.

# SHOW PREPARATION

Winning at shows requires careful planning and skilful management of the birds. There is little hope of consistent winning unless the fancier sets out to achieve high standards at all times. In the first place the stock must comply with the *standards* and breed true to type. Newcomers often believe that they can produce a winning strain within a very short time and get quite frustrated when, after many attempts, the exhibits fail to win because they are not as good as the birds they were bred from.

Crossing with unknown strains is the cause of most failures because introducing new blood mixes up the genes with resultant non-standard offspring of varying colours and other features. There has to be a stable breeding programme and line breeding and in-breeding (carefully controlled) will be essential. Both aim to fix the required characteristics so that winning stock can be produced each year. It is often argued that inbreeding results in a loss of stamina and laying powers and this is correct, but the experienced breeder uses the same strain yet selects breeding stock so they are not too closely related. As a result, the same strain is kept and bred from without losing the high quality achieved.

The author has seen many famous strains being bred for decades, but once the original breeder ceases to carry on, the quality is lost because the new owners no longer know the master plan which has been used with success. Thus purchasing a particular strain from a breeder who has acquired them, may be unsuccessful simply because the stock has been bred in a different way.

There is no shortage of information on the methods to employ for a specific breed*. Some require 'double mating' which means using one breeding pen for pullets and another for cockerels. Others advocate methods of obtaining a specific colour or a certain shape or other features as described earlier in Chapter 3, under *Key Factors.*

---

* The publisher can offer general books; eg, *Bantams & Small Poultry*, or such titles as *Understanding Old English Game, The Rhode Island Red, The Orpington Fowl, etc.*

# Getting Birds Fit

If the correct type of bird is being bred, which possesses all the key factors, there is a very good chance of success, provided they are fit, without any physical defects or ailments such as *Scaley Leg* mite or other problems.

The essentials are:

1. Provide a Dust Bath for regular use, supplemented by periodic dusting or spraying with louse or mite killer.

2. Wash birds fairly regularly and especially before a show.

3. Rub vaseline or olive oil on the legs and rub well in; any sign of coarse scales or powder on the legs will call for rubbing with a suitable ointment (eg, sulphur ointment if available), which is rubbed in after a thorough wash.

4. Give a tonic if birds look out of condition; a *Multi-vitamin Extra* is available which contains vitamins B2, B6, B12, C, E, K3, and various acids. Some fanciers give cod liver oil on the mixed corn or pellets.

5. Feed a balanced diet which would include pellets, mixed corn for the hard feathered breeds, and a plentiful supply of greenstuff. Give the appropriate food for the age of the stock and if wishing to get cockerels into top condition feed layers' pellets and give them a limited run. Chick weed, grass clippings, garden weeds. and even dried leaves all give the birds essential food as well as exercise by scratching for morsels.

Birds kept outside with plenty of natural food, including grass come into condition very well, but shade must be provided or the colours will fade or with white birds become brassy. Contrary to what might be expected birds intended for showing should not run wild on free range or they will never become tame or in top condition. Semi-intensive is more acceptable because birds become tame and can be watched more carefully. Periodically, especially the male birds, they should be placed in training pens, so they become accustomed to being handled and can be trained to stand correctly.

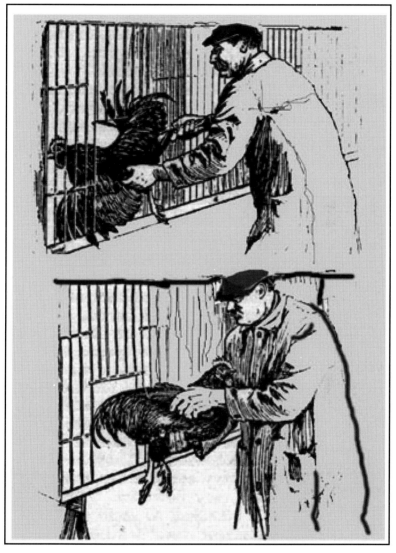

*Above:* Incorrect Handling which will damage feathers.
*Bottom:* Correct Handling; catch the bird and gently turn it round to come out head first. Practise on birds to make sure they are not frightened at judging time. Many birds fail because they are afraid and wild.

## Selection of the Food

Food for exhibits should be selected on the basis of whether hard feathered or soft. There is also the medium type which are close feathered and yet are not exactly either hard or soft in the plumage.Thus a possible classification would be as follows:

*1. Soft Feathered*

This would include all the feathery types which are expected to have a profusion of feathers. For example—Brahmas, Dorkings, Cochins, Orpingtons, Pekins, Plymouth Rocks, Sussex, and Wyandottes.

*2. Hard Feathered*

The feathers are close to the body with as little fluff as possible. This category includes Aseel, Indian Game (Cornish), Malays, Modern Game, Old English Game, Shamos and other Game birds.

*3. Medium Feathered*

These breeds have reasonably plentiful feathering, but are not as profuse as category 1 or as close as 2. The classification is somewhat arbitrary and with some breeds an argument can be put forward to include them in one of the other categories. They include the Mediterranean breeds such as Leghorn and Minorca, Campines, Croad Langshan, Hamburghs, Old English Pheasant Fowl, Polands, Redcaps, and Welsummers. Sebright and Rosecomb bantams are also included.

Not all breeds have been listed, but the reader should be able to see what is required. The suggestion is that the adult Soft Feathered breeds should be fed mash or pellets with around 15 per cent protein and little or no corn.

With hard feathered only mixed corn is usually advocated, thus giving the birds around 10 per cent protein plus any vitamins from greenstuff. The author does not entirely agree with this approach because it can lead to feathers becoming very brittle and tending to break. A small amount of layers' pellets during the laying season is a better approach because it is when the birds are renewing their feathers, that mashes are  recommended, but for

*maintenance* of the plumage and the feed requirements for ***breeding*** the extra protein and vitamins are essential.

The ***medium category*** of birds will certainly need pellets for
egg production or for fattening, but mixed corn will help to keep
the plumage tight and not too profuse. When dealing with bantams
such as Sebrights and Rosecombs the mixed diet will be ideal.

Some breeders recommend that maize (yellow corn) should
not be fed to breeds which have white legs or skin because this
affects the colouring. Undoubtedly this is true if fed in large quan-
tities, but it must be remembered that maize does include important
vitamins, so a little may be beneficial.

At show time the soft feathered birds may be given a mid-
day meal of bread soaked in milk and then squeezed out so the
birds can peck it. Hard boiled eggs crumbled in to the mixture can
also be beneficial during the training period.

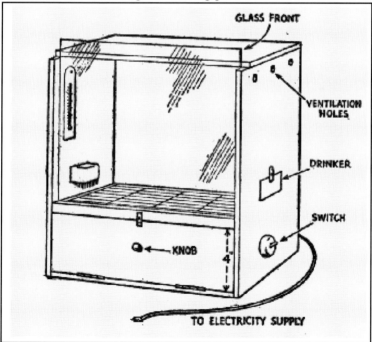

**Cage Which can be Used for Drying**

## Training the Birds

A few weeks before a show it is usual to start the final training of the birds expected to be entered. The correct period for training should be long enough for conditioning , but not too long or the birds become fat and lethargic. The time of year also affects the optimum period because in the winter months birds can be kept in limited space, and have artificial light, yet suffer no ill effects.

In the warm summer months birds suffer from *dry hackle, northern mite,* and other problems from being confined in rooms with inadequate air flow.

The usual requirements are:

1. A Penning/Training room or shed.

2. An outside covered cockerel pen which can be moved around so the single bird can get plenty of grass as well as exercise.

## The  Penning Room

For the small fancier this should be of a size which allows about a dozen birds to be kept in special training units. Around 2 X 2 metres is adequate. However, with the breeder who keeps hundreds of birds,  the size should be scaled up so that one wall can be a long line of show pens.

The pen/cage doors must be large enough to take the birds out without trouble. Shavings are put on the floor and a drinking container is hooked on the front. This should be large enough for the size of the bird and it should be appreciated that the small drinking containers made for cage birds are far too small even for bantams. Yet without a plentiful supply of water the birds will very quickly lose condition.

Food should also be kept in a container on the front of the wires and care taken not to over feed, otherwise birds get sluggish and fat. Greenstuff  can help to keep the birds fit. As noted, not keeping too long in the training can also be beneficial; fortunately, once birds become tame, they become quite friendly and this lasts.

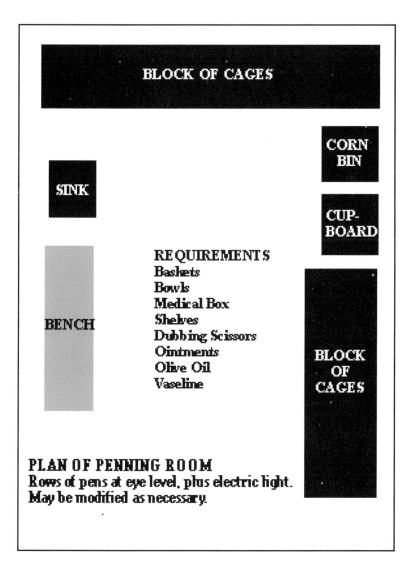

BLOCK OF CAGES

CORN BIN

SINK

CUP-BOARD

BENCH

REQUIREMENTS
Baskets
Bowls
Medical Box
Shelves
Dubbing Scissors
Ointments
Olive Oil
Vaseline

BLOCK OF CAGES

**PLAN OF PENNING ROOM**
Rows of pens at eye level, plus electric light.
May be modified as necessary.

The process of taming should start when chicks are being reared. Feed the chicks indoors and get them to feed from your hand; give them special titbits at lunch time—scraps of bacon, bread and cooked potatoes are all acceptable, provided only about 20 per cent is given in the total intake.

In the evening go into the sheds and lift birds from their perches and talk to them as you assess their condition. When they go into the training pens carry out the same procedure because they become quite tame in the semi-darkness or artificial light.

### Using  A Judging Stick

Birds should be trained in the art of standing in the appropriate position for the breed. A bird which is supposed to stand high should be encouraged to be in this stance; those of low stature should be trained to stand in the correct way.

### Examples

*Modern Game*— Use the judging stick to gently position the head and then the breast, and keep repeating this process until the bird automatically stands in position. Do not put the stick across the back which will have the opposite effect.

*Cochins, Pekins, Dutch bantams, Japanese bantams, etc*—All birds of low stature— place the judging stick point on the back and encourage the birds to relax and not rise up. Do not use the stick to make these breeds stand higher and look taller; the standard carriage does not expect them to look tall.

In all cases make sure the wings are in the correct position and if necessary stroke them back so they do not appear too low.

Much of this process will take time and patience so that when the show comes along the birds are tame and exhibit themseles to the best advantage.

At this stage keep checking that individual birds have no defects such as broken wing feathers or feathers of the wrong colour. It is permissible to remove defective feathers, but allow a few weeks for new ones to grow.

# Washing & Grooming

About 2-3 weeks before a show it is usual to give light coloured birds a thorough wash and double rinse. Some breeders also advocate washing all birds, whether light or dark in plumage.

Provided sufficient time is allowed for the feathers to be thoroughly dry and look natural, there is much to recommend washing. Some exhibitors do not like the chore and make the excuse that dark birds are better for not being immersed in water with the consequent loss of oils in the plumage.Under no circumstances should smelly, dishevelled, dirty birds be presented for judging—the judge would be quite justified in 'passing' such exhibits. Yet such specimens are still presented and are no credit to the owners.

Washing is usually referred to as *The Three Bowl Technique* on the grounds that three separate bowls or small baths are required for completion of the task. Wash the legs *first* and then proceed:

1. *Bath 1*.

Use quite warm water and washing up liquid is added at a temperature that will allow hand contact, rather like the approach adopted for washing dishes.The water should be hot enough to remove any dirt, but not to cause discomfort to the birds. A sponge and soft brush should be used fairly vigorously following the line of growth; care must be taken not to damage feathers.

The bath should be deep enough to immerse the birds quite thorougly including the neck, but obviously avoiding the eyes.

2. *Bath 2.*

Rinse in warm water cooler than the first wash. The purpose is to remove all traces of soap and check that all parts are clean.

3. *Final Rinse Bath.*

This will be filled with luke warm water and some add a conditioner which for white birds would be a blue rinse. Different solutions are suggested by fanciers, but it must be remembered that if taken too far the bird may become fluorescent or some form of dye may be left which is illegal. It may be better to add nothing.

## Drying

Once the rinse is completed the bird has to be dried which means squeezing the water from the plumage and wrapping a towel around the bird to achieve reasonable dryness which can be completed by using a hand hardryer or blow heater in the penning room. Alternatively, for bantams, a drying cage may be used. In warm weather, provided semi-dryness is achieved first, the drying will occur naturally. At first the birds will shake and shiver, but if in a sunny position in the penning room, they will dry quickly and should feel no ill effects.

Dry shavings should be provided and removed and renewed when the drying is completed. Alternatively, a cardboard base can be inserted so any surplus water soaks away and this is discarded and replaced with a thick covering of white wood shavings.

## Final Touches

The final touches consist of checks on plumage and then going on to give special treatment to the following:

1. Using a silk cloth gently stroke the plumage to bring back the shine, but only when birds are absolutely dry. Make sure all the feathers are lying in a natural fashion.

2. Apply a face cream to bring up the red and improve the appearance. Olive oil rubbed on and then removed is a common application. Mixtures of alcohol, camphorated oil, glycerine and citric acid have all been suggested, but a trial run on a bird is advised and take care not to use any mixture when the after effects can be seen at the show. The mildest of oils may cause a comb to shed its skin (flaking) after a few days, so any application is best just prior to the show. With birds having **head points,** such as Rosecomb bantams, the lobes should be washed in milk and then dried; some add boracic ointment or talcum powder, but make sure all is rubbed in before penning at the show.

3. Remove any ingrained dirt on the legs by rubbing with olive oil. In desperate cases some breeders advocate removing and

dirt from inder the scales by using a toothpick, but this is a danger-
ous practice and birds to be shown should not be allowed to get in
this state just before a show. If it does occur then it would be better
to substitute another bird and then hope the first choice can be treated
with ointment to remove all ingrained dirt before the next show.

On the day of the show, check the legs and wipe them over,
also possibly applying the face cream and rubbing off all surplus.
Do not try to add colour or feathers or improve the comb because
any falsifying would be regarded as faking.

In carrying out these preparations an assistant will be found
to be invaluable. Birds can be held whilst the second person applies
all that is needed. Various devices have been used and one appli-
ance for securing bantams is shown below.

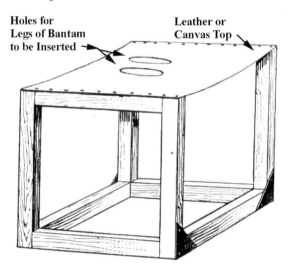

**A Hammock for holding a Bantam**
This is easily made from wood and can stand on a table or bench whilst the
bantam receives the show preparation.
Designed by Joseph Shakespeare a bantam expert (USA).

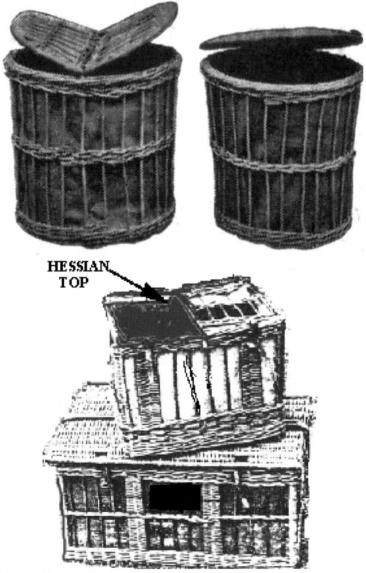

Above: Round Baskets—avoid spoiling tail.
Below: Baskets with Compartments.

## Taking to The Show

Once birds are ready they are taken to the show in suitable boxes or baskets which should be of adequate size for the birds to turn and breathe easily. Make sure there is adequate ventilation and no direct sunlight on the baskets to excessive heat and distress to the birds.

The baskets should be well littered with shavings or straw so the birds have a copmfortable journey. It is usual to feed and water before putting them in the baskets and if a long journey is involved bread moistened with milk or water will tide them over until fed by the stewards at the show.

On arrival, book in the birds with the show manager or secretary, and then make sure they are placed in the correct pens. If rings are sent these should have been placed upside down on the leg of the bird in accordance with instructions. Once penned, birds should be left for judging and on no account be handled and taken out of the pen; neither should any birds belonging to other exhibitors be touched for this can lead to misunderstandings.

The show schedule and entry slip will show the position of each class so there should be no problems in locating the correct position and if in doubt enquire from a steward, because any mistakes can lead to a bird being *passed* for being in the wrong class.

### Returning From the Show

Once the show ends birds must be removed and cleared through the stewards and taken back for a well earned rest. They should be examined and placed in the training pens for about a week. Hampers should be cleaned out and litter burned. Periodically varnish or creosote baskets so they last and do not harbour mice.

The first day, feed a soft food such as bread and milk and then normal food will start. Once a quarantine period has elapsed they can be returned to their normal runs, but check to make sure there is no fighting or bullying, especially with Game birds which will be aggressive even after a short period of absence.

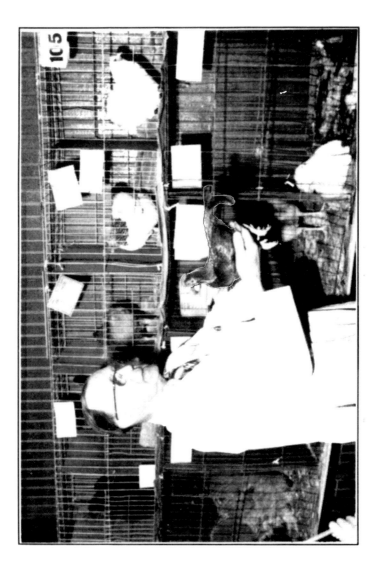

# 11

# THE
# JUDGING OF POULTRY

*Judges they say are born: I wonder.*

W Powell-Owen
*Many times President of the Poultry Club.*

**<u>Opposite</u>**

An Experienced Judge in Action
James Barr a Scottish Judge

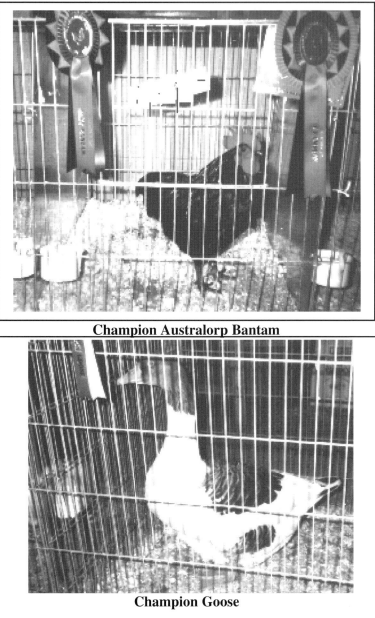

**Champion Australorp Bantam**

**Champion Goose**

## METHODS OF JUDGING
There are two main methods of judging poultry:

**1. Comparisons Method**, but using the official standards to select the main show features. It is a process of selection to decide the order of merit by spotting the presence of required attributes and deducting and faults or defects.

**2. Points Method (possibly with the Grading Method)** which is similar to 1. above, but the main features (Key factors) are given a numerical value, and possibly an order of merit value—A, B, C, etc, and the points are added with deductions for faults, thus arriving at a specific figure for each exhibit.

This latter system is used in all sorts of situations and is even popular for selecting staff to fit a specfic situation—there is a *Seven Point Plan* and a *Five Point Plan* which allow characteristics of a position to be listed and given a numerical value which is then compared with the actual values allotted to applicants for a job. Provided the methods are used by experienced people they work quite well. However, it should not be thought that the approach necessarily gives better results. What it does give is a foundation in specific terms which allows others to agree or disagree with the results of the assessment.

Irrespective of the method used, judgement or opinion is essential and any judging must try to be as *objective* as possible. Poor decisions are usually due to a judge being biased or being too subjective by applying his or her preferences rather than those shown in the Standard. Allocating numerical points to exhibits still requires the application of opinion and judgement so an error can still be made.

## The Points Systems
These are used in the USA and on the Continent and special cards are used. In Britain judging Utility breeds may also be on a points system; judging eggs may be along the same lines, but can also be on the Comparisons Method. A variation is the Grading System, giving descriptions (eg Excellent) with comments.

The USA system of marking is somewhat varied  because the 100 points are divided in a different fashion. The main features are listed under 16 main features, each of which is divided into 'Shape' and 'Colour'. These are Size, Symmetry, Condition, Beak, Comb, Head & Face, Eyes, Wattles, Ear Lobes, Neck, Back, Wings, Tail, Breast, Body & Fluff, Legs & Toes.

Thus *Back* carries 12 points,  divided into 8 for **shape** and  4 for **colour** for a White bird and 6 + 6 for a Coloured Bird, ie, other than White. For *Legs & Toes* the mixture is 5 shape and 3 for colour on all birds

## The Grading System*

The outline given above is, in effect, combining the award of prizes on relative superiority —First, Second, Third and Fourth prizes— with the system used on the Continent where birds are graded according to the merits of each.

In the full grading system each bird is assessed and placed in a category such as  Excellent, Very Good, Good, Moderate.

A brief summary of all the Key Features is included on the award so that fanciers and club officials can see the merits of each exhibit. The cards may be attached to the outside of the pens so any one can see whether the exhibit is top class.

This system may also be combined with awarding prizes so that the two methods still show the order of merit. This is useful because there may be a few birds in a class which are, say, *Excellent,* but could still be graded into **First, Second** and **Third.**

The main problem with the Grading System is the detailed analysis required, following the main headings of the Standard. This scrutiny by segments pinpoints the ***Strengths and Weaknesses*** of

---

* See The Grade System of Judging, Fred Hams, *The Poultry Club Year Book,* **1984.**

birds, but it takes up a great deal of time and the findings have to be recorded on cards or other records. Obviously, more judging time will be essential to cope.**

Overall, the grading system, used properly, can be used to establish a method which is consistent and fair.

# AWARD STRUCTURE

In recent times much controversy has arisen from the method of awarding *Best in Show*. Not all prize winners are of the same quality and therefore fanciers argue that some form of weighting is desirable. However, all are agreed that irrespective of the method used there should be prizes for FIRST, SECOND and THIRD with distinctive coloured cards for each grade.

The next stage is the *best for each breed* and then selection of the reserve in the opposite sex. *Bests* and *Reserves* in hard feather, soft feather, bantams, true bantams, rare breeds, and other classifications should follow.

The Best in Show should be selected from the Bests in all breeds; this will then allow the Reserve (Opposite Sex?) to be selected. In the USA standards the rules state specifically that only those winning first prizes shall be eligible for top awards.

Special Awards usually follow the rules regarding the trophy concerned.

A typical set of general awards would be:

**Show Champion, Reserve Show Champion, Champion Large Fowl— Soft Feather, Champion Large Fowl—Hard Feather, Champion Bantam—Soft Feather, Champion Bantam—Hard Feather, Champion True Bantam, Champion Trio, Champion Juvenile, Champion Eggs, Champion Waterfowl, Champion Turkey, Champion Rare Breed.**

---

** **Another approach is offered by John Craft in** *The Poultry Club Year Book,* **1997 entitled** *Grading Poultry.*

## Comparisons Method

A judge proceeds around the exhibits and views them for type, ie overall shape, size and carriage. This is the first stage of selecting the likely winners.

Next comes assessment of merit and in a negative fashion how far a bird falls short of the ideal. In assessing the birds some judges use judging sticks to test for tameness and for establishing whether a particular bird appears to be the correct type and whether it stands well. Serious faults like duck-footedness in Old English Game or smudge marks on Sebrights, or lack of tail in a Brahma are all examples of defects. Many more are listed in an earlier chapter.

If there is doubt on some feature a judge should always handle each exhibit. In fact, it is better if *all* birds are lifted out of the cage or pen at the show and handled to see whether there are such faults as broken features, crooked breast bone, split wing, presence of mite or over or under weight. Each will have its own known characteristics. For example, with OEG a bird should be firm and plump, but also muscular: the large Game fancier expects his birds to be "light and corky".

Tameness is vital for a wild bird never shows itself properly. Obvious features such as comb, tail and legs should be examined to make sure that there are no faults.

Ideally the judge should be judging to the standards; some do, others have an overall picture of the requirements and judge on these; which is probably the most usual approach. One prominent judge has stated:

> **"As far as I know few people have ever judged exhibition poultry against the written Standards".**

This statement may be rather too positive because many judges *do* study the Standards and use them as a basis for making awards, but possibly not consciously or not in an obvious fashion to the observer. A fact not realized by clubs is that judges may believe that the presence of a book of Standards show a weakness, a lack of knowledge.

## Need to Know the Standards Thoroughly

A judge must know the detailed standard or he cannot be fair.  Moreover, he should know all the major faults so that a bird with serious shortcomings is *not* made best of breed and even best in show!

The procedures are fairly standard:

**1. The show secretary hands out pre-prepared judging sheets in a ring binder.**

**2. If required a steward is appointed to assist the judge.**

**3. Judging is usually a quick survey of the class to make sure the entrants agree with the judging sheet. Any errors are communicated to the secretary or show manager so that a decision can be made on the apparent discrepancies. If there are very few entries in two related classes then these may be merged—much depends on the rules being followed.**

*A systematic approach is essential and each judge will form his own views and develop his system. Armed with a list of exhibits in a class, entered in numerical order, the judge will usually walk down the aisle and establish the extent of the birds to be judged; eg, Sebright Bantams, Male.*

*At the same time,  the birds should be checked to make sure that there are no oddities which have appeared in the class by mistake; wrong breed, wrong colour, sick birds, and any other anomalies should be brought to the attention of the Show Secretary for a decision on what  should be done. Any sick birds should be removed by the Secretary and isolated to avoid any spreading of disease. There is also the public to think of ; if a bird looks as if it is dying the show organizers could be blamed,  even though they have had no part  in its condition.*

*Arriving at the placing of birds in order of merit can be done fairly quickly by the process of elimination of the faulty specimens.*
**Cont. Next page**

**4.** The *procedure* may take the following form:

(i) Look at each bird and decide which do not comply with the essential standard in the Key Factors, eg, shape or colour.

**5.** Note major faults and decide which are below prize winning standard. *Write* the main faults on the judging sheet so that there is a ready reference if an exhibitor in a friendly way wishes to know the main problems with his (losing) bird OR in case of a dispute and subsequent enquiry, by the show committee of the Club or Poultry Club.

**6.** The exhibits should be taken out of the show pen and inspected:

(a) Condition—any serious ailments should disqualify;

(b) Shape—must comply with standard in silhouette, size, and stance.

(c) Colouring— wrong shade or wrong colours to be penalized;

(d) Faults* as revealed by a detailed examination:

*** Examine plumage and main parts such as wings and tail;

***Look around the vent and in hackle, etc, for signs of lice or mite; look to see if feathers eaten—tiny holes;

***Look at legs — note whether scaley legs, wrong colour, duck footed, back toe not touching ground, twisted toes;

*** Examine face—correct face colours, comb and lobes correct type, no trimming or faking, beak not weak;

*** Look at all features and make sure that *as a whole* the bird is worthy of a prize and do not give a first prize to a bird which has major failings.

---

*See Chapter 9, *Likely Defects*, which gives a detailed coverage of main faults likely to be found.

When defective judging is spotted, such as giving a bird a top award even though it has serious faults, it is usual to receive a reply to the effect that **Comparison Judging** means selecting the ***best from the exhibits on show.***

Giving **Best in Show** to an exhibit which has gained first prize in a class of three birds when there are other classes with large numbers is also a very doubtful practice and sensible judges will avoid this situation. It is not beyond the authorities to devise a system which gives a weighting to prize winners which acknowledges the number in the class. Surely a **First** in a class of 25 birds must be worth more than a similar award where there is a class of four?

Many obvious discrepancies can be seen at shows. The specimens given in Chapter 9 exhibiting faults are mainly past prize winners and yet they display failings which should have been obvious.*

Imagine an OEG cock with his back toe off the ground when he is standing upright (a recent photograph of Best in Show had this fault!) or an Ancona male with short legs and very few tips.

On Anconas the judge should look for

> **"Type: a bird evenly balanced, with a good head piece, full fronted and clean in both white and bottle green. Tipping should be seen without the aid of a magnifying glass".***

This short paragraph is a summary of the standard and as such serves to guide an exhibitor on the essential requirements. Unfortunately despite standards being constantly updated and improved ***personal preferences do affect the end result.***

On colour, what is a good "Buff" ? Should it be an even fawn colour or a colour approaching orange?  Surely there should be a clear definition!

On **barring** is the Barred Rock to be precise in markings or is the overall impression and colour to be the criterion. Should 'Cuckoo' and 'Barred' be more clearly explained?

---

* *Judging Anconas* **D H Ferguson Thomas, Past President of the Ancona Club** .(*Poultry Club Year Book* **1968**).

## AWARDING THE PRIZES

As noted, judging poultry involves the process of comparing one bird with another and, collectively, one bird with all the others in the class. The former comparison takes place once the first few top birds have been selected; the final selection into third, second and first is then done and if the class is large enough, highly commended and commended would be awarded.

The purpose is to place birds in order of merit and it should be appreciated that this does not always mean that birds awarded first and second prizes are really first rate birds. They are the best on the day, but, if all exhibits are of poor quality, the first prize winner could still have serious faults.

Judges should learn to be strict (although not harshly so) and the really poor specimens should be passed over and if, at the end of the time, there are no reasonable exhibits a first prize should *not* be awarded.

The status of the show should affect the quality of exhibits. A national show will call for top quality birds, but a small local show may not be able to attract the same top class birds. Accordingly, any fancier buying birds which show a prize card should note the name and the number of the class. If there are only three birds in a class, being third means nothing but it is a different story if there are 20 exhibits.

## Special Awards

There is a diverse and wide variety of special prizes which may be awarded at club and national shows. Besides the elaborate show cards and rosettes there are cups and trophies, some given in memory of past breeders or by present enthusastic breeders who wish to publicize their own particular strains. The art of sponsorship is well known in all activities.

These special awards serve a useful purpose although on occasions it might be better to have small replicas made which the winners can keep and let the valuable cups be kept locked away in a safe place.

## THE JUDGE

A poultry show judge is one elected by the particular breed club or is one who appears on a Judges Panel and is appointed by show organisers to adjudicate on the day in question. If a large show, then there should be a number of specialist judges. If relatively small, one judge and a steward may suffice, but even then with, say, 100 entries the process will take upwards of one hour and I have seen a conscientious judge take the whole morning, taking each bird out of the show cage and then making comparisons can be quite time consuming.

For the British Poultry Club and American Poultry Association there are written examinations to be passed as well as tests and practice sessions. It is a length process because it takes many years of experience to be able to know the standard and decide which bird in a class of birds is the one nearest to the ideal as laid down by the breed club and main Poultry Club.

Some judges make a decision on how a bird appears from outside the pen, which is not really acceptable because faults not always apparent, may be revealed on handling. Colour faults can be detected by examining the feathers; faulty wings and tail can be seen; broken feathers; faking*; bumps on breast or back, and general 'lightness' all become apparent.

When dealing with large Old English Game the accepted practice was to balance the cock bird in the hand to make sure he felt 'corky' and was well balanced. This stems from the fighting days, which is not really applicable today. However, which ever approach is adopted, it is essential to ensure that Game birds are broad at the front and very narrow at the back and the latter is short.

---

*The days of faking as described in *The Art of Faking Exhibition Poultry*, George Ryley Scott, appeared to be a thing of the past, but I have had recent reports from judges of 'operations' on combs (rosecombs were involved) and Old English Game with new sickle feathers being super-glued into the shaft of the old feathers. If practices of this nature are discovered the exhibitor should be disqualified from showing, instead of being 'overlooked'.

## Number of Judges

On occasions suggestions have been made that two judges should be involved with *each class,* thus indicating there has been no prejudice. The subject has been aired at great length by various authorities going right back to the heyday of Lewis Wright who was in favour of a single judge. A summary of the advantages claimed for a single judge are:

**1. Each judge is responsible for the awards made.**

**2. Tests have shown that single judges work quicker and give satisfactory results, provided they are not overworked.**

**3. Each judge can be selected for his expertise in particular breeds.**

Nevertheless, there are possible disadvantages. Not all fanciers want to take on the responsibility and until he or she acquires the necessary experience and confidence some form of apprenticeship might be appropriate. At present the system allows a would-be judge to start with one breed and then expand into others, thus gradually getting more experience.

Another problem that arises is the fact that the same judges continue to officiate for tens of years or more and there is a danger they are out of date. In fact, some judges in the past have not even been breeding poultry any more and there have even been cases where a judge has brought in birds for showing (when he is not judging), but has never bred them.

## Method of Approach

Judges and stewards must behave with dignity and display a sense of fairness. They must not be influenced by stock being exhibited which originated from them or for which they know the owner. Unfortunately, in the close world of breed clubs, where the top breeders are known, and they are often judges, there is a danger of what might be termed 'unfair relationships'. All kinds of arrangements are possible, even to the extent of birds being loaned to enter in the show when the lender is judging. Fortunately, these cases appear to be few in number, but they have to be watched and, if supported evidence can be supplied, the matter should be reported to the Poultry Club.

As a means of adding dignity and to avoid misunderstanding the judge and his steward wear white coats. These also help to keep the clothing of the officials quite clean. During the judging session there should be no conversations with other people whether they are officials or outsiders; in fact, a sound practice is to bar all members of the public from the exhibition hall until judging is completed. Any attemps made by exhibitors to influence judging should be dealt with firmly—unfortunately the enthusiasm and wish to win leads some exhibitors to get carried away so they make rash statements or inadvisable actions, which afterwards they regret.*

Anger and resentment at the awards is quite common and judges may lose 'friends' in the process. Yet any judge should be able to justify his awards to the satisfaction of everybody and can always explain the reasons to the disgruntled exhibitor—the remarks on the *judging sheet*, explained earlier in the chapter, should be the basis for the result. Fanciers must be prepared to accept results or not show!

## Payment for Judging

Clubs are not usually endowed with plentiful funds and for that reason judges carry out duties for a small fee which may cover expenses, although often not. In a hobby situation this is understandable, but not all judges can afford to subsidize a club and therefore if at all possible a reasonable sum should be paid.

Fortunately, judging also gives social contact with friends and fellow breeders and this often makes the event worthwhile.

---

\* **Many years ago the author when judging received threats from an over keen fancier who was asked to leave the tent. In fact, the birds in question, which were not known by him, received high awards anyway, and the exhibitor, came and apologized for his behaviour. No further action was needed!**

Some regional shows, organized by societies, have a friendly lunch for judges and club officials and this is very pleasant and allows discussion of results so far. At the end of judging the top awards have to be made on a joint basis and early contact with the rest of the judges can be useful.

### JUDGING DUCKS & GEESE

The same general rules apply to ducks and geese as for fowls, although the large breeds of geese are rather difficult to remove from the pens. Often they are penned at ground level so they can be seen and moved around with a judging stick.

The standard for each breed will be followed and typical faults in existence will be the basis of elimination of poor specimens and through a process of attrition the best will remain. In table birds, including geese, size, type and weight are usually the deciding factors.

With the laying breeds such as Khaki Campbells and Runner Ducks there should be signs of good health and an active constitution.

Pen training is still required and the exhibits should be quite clean when penned. An analysis is made as follows:

**Buff Orpington
Correct Type.
Long, deep body.
well balanced
for eggs & meat.**

*Possible Faults which might be present on an imperfect duck:*
**1. Small Size.
2. Upright or horizontal body.
3. Roach back
& pronounced Keel.
4. Imperfect colouring.**

This would be done for each breed, thus arriving at the ideal and the faults.*

## JUDGING EGGS

Judging eggs requires a practised skill as well as knowledge on shape, size and quality contents. Standards are laid down for judges and exhibitors to follow covering fowls, bantams, ducks, geese and turkeys.

Eggs are judged externally and then broken in a manner which does not damage the yolk so the contents can be examined. The recommended method is to use a light blunt knife to form a gash and then gently tip the contents on to a plate.**

The egg should be fresh with a small air space; the yolk should be golden yellow, nicely rounded on top, and the albumen quite distinct in outline with the yolk in a central position. If the yolk is wrinkled and flat this is a sure sign of a stale egg. This is also the case when the albumen is thin and watery. Blood spots or other defects will incur penalties and so will the wrong colour shell—usually caused by the foodstuff given. Grass is extremely good for adding colour, but if carried too far will can give the albumen a green cast.          An example follows.

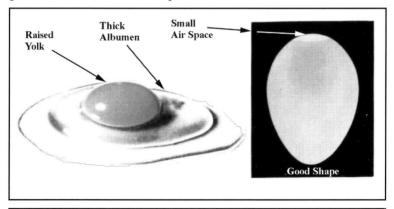

* A detailed analysis is to be found for each breed in the book written by the present author: *Domesticated Ducks & Geese,* **Third edition, 1996.**
** W Powell-Owen, probably the greatest expert on judging poultry and eggs.

## JUDGING TURKEYS

There are many breeds of turkeys , some purely utility and others more the fancy or exhibition type. Usually they are judged on size for the utility breeds and on the colour and other standard features for the remainder.

**Prize Bronze Turkey as drawn by Ernest Wippell**

Commercialization and the development of the broad breast has done much to change the form of the turkey. A large bronze would be in the region of 16 kilos so great weight would be the main criterion, whereas the smaller breeds such as Bourbon Red, Buff, or Slate would be much lighter.

Type, including size, carries 40 points with the head and colour being awarded 20 each. In the absence of serious faults the carriage and size will usually prevail. For a detailed analysis and descriptions, readers are referred to *Keeping Turkeys*, J Barnes,1997.

### JUDGING UTILITY BIRDS

Shows are generally confined to what are termed "Exhibition Birds", although quite often utility features are indicated in the standards and the judges should take this in to account. Regretfully, breeds like the Black Orpingtons and Dorkings have been spoilt by neglect of the laying powers, yet Buff Orpingtons are still quite commercialty oriented.

Utility birds can still be attractive, but not to the neglect of the factors which made the breeds of great commercial value. Excessive feathering, tallness, and great size of bone and other factors all contributed to their downfall.

Interest in utility fowl was quite widespread, but nowadays is in the process of being revived.

A pioneer and leader of poultry breeding and judging was W Powell-Owen who played a leading part until the 1950s. He developed standards and special methods for assessing the merits of birds.

The form overleaf was designed by W Powell-Owen.

*He developed a score card which allowed fowls to be judged on their potential. Although there were criticisms of the concept there is little doubt that the instigator did much useful work and improved the position of utility poultry breeds.*

*W PO developed a system of measuring the breast, the pelvic area, width of back, length of back, and so on. These measurements, which were based on the finger as a unit of measurement, showed the 'Capacity' and the 'Capability'. On the show side, marks were awarded for Condition, Health, Size, and Breed Characters.*

*The grand total from the different categories was the basis for the award.*

## THE "POWELL-OWEN" UTILITY SCORE-CARD

| CAPACITY | Fingers | Points | Awarded |
|---|---|---|---|
| End of breast-bone to pelvic | 1 | 4 | |
| | 2 | 8 | |
| | 3 | 12 | |
| | 4 | 16 | |
| | 5 | 20 | |
| Between pelvic bones | 2 | 2½ | |
| | 3 | 5 | |
| Between pelvic and tail bone | 1 | 5 | |
| | 2 | 10 | |
| Width of back | medium | 3 | |
| | good | 6 | |
| | v. good | 10 | |
| Length of back | medium | 2½ | |
| | good | 5 | |
| Width between legs | medium | 3 | |
| | good | 6 | |
| | v. good | 10 | |
| Length, depth and width of abdomen | medium | 3 | |
| | good | 6 | |
| | v. good | 10 | |
| Total | | 70 | |

| CAPABILITY | | Points |
|---|---|---|
| Pelvic bone | v. thick | 3 |
| | thick | 6 |
| | thin | 9 |
| | v. thin | 12 |
| | If straight add | 3 |
| Flesh | coarse | 5 |
| | medium | 10 |
| | fine | 15 |
| Vent | size | 5 |
| | fineness | 5 |
| Head points | medium | 3 |
| | good | 6 |
| | v. good | 10 |
| Bone and horn | coarse | 3 |
| | medium | 6 |
| | v. good | 10 |
| Feather | excess | 3 |
| | medium | 6 |
| | ideal | 10 |
| Exhibitor........................... | | |
| Breed............... Sex......... | | |
| Class No...... Pen No....... | | |
| Total | | 70 |

| BREED CHARACTERS, ETC. | Points | Awarded |
|---|---|---|
| Show condition ................. | 10 | |
| Health ............................ | 10 | |
| Size (ideal utility) ............. | 10 | |
| Breed characters ............... | 30 | |
| Total | 60 | |

| GRAND TOTAL | |
|---|---|
| Capacity .......................... | 70 |
| Capability ....................... | 70 |
| Breed characters, etc. ......... | 60 |
| Total | 200 |

## The Utility Judging Card for Utility Poultry

POULTRY BOOKS
BY Dr JOSEPH BATTY
*The Silkie Fowl*
*Old English Game Bantams*
*Understanding Modern Game*
(with James Bleazard)
*Understanding Indian Game*
(with Ken Hawkey)
*Bantams & Small Poultry*
*Poultry Ailments*
*Sussex & Dorking Fowl*
*Sebright Bantams*
*Poultry Characteristics—Tails*
*Artificial Incubation & Rearing*
*Natural Incubation & Rearing*
*Domesticated Ducks & Geese*
*The Ancona Fowl*
*Ostrich Farming*
*Concise Poultry Colour Guide*
*Japanese Long Tailed Fowl*
*Poultry Shows & Showing*
*Natural Poultry Keeping*
*Understanding Old English Game*
*The Orpington Fowl (With Will Burdett)*
*The Minorca Fowl*
*The Rhode Island Fowl*

# INDEX